UNDERSTANDING AMPLITUDE MODULATION

by IRVING M. GOTTLIEB

PREFACE

Amplitude modulation is uniquely interesting. Its emergence as an important function of applied electronics was the inevitable result of the ability of a vacuum tube to amplify, oscillate, and rectify, which aided the development of radio. In fact, amplitude modulation and radio grew up together, and later television evolved much as the consequence of more sophisticated amplitude-modulation techniques. It is now true that amplitude modulation is also significantly involved in industrial electronics, instrumentation, and telemetry.

Technically, as well as historically, amplitude modulation is the natural prelude to the study of other modulating methods. The author feels that previous literature on amplitude modulation tends toward one of two categories. One finds, in abundance, excessive mathematical treatment without practical considerations. At the opposite extreme is found a pitifully superficial approach to the subject. Neither orientation is satisfactory for the individual who works with equipment and must understand the vital interplay between principle and practice.

It is therefore the intended purpose of this text to present theory in terms of practical implementation, and to discuss practice in the light of theoretical support. This approach has been pursued with the needs of students, technicians, and servicemen in mind. The author has also endeavored to serve the interests of radio amateurs, citizens band enthusiasts, and others engrossed in electronic experimentation and design.

IRVING M. GOTTLIEB

CONTENTS

CHAPTER 1

CHAPTER 2

CHAPTER 3

CHAPTER 4

Chapter 1

FUNDAMENTALS

In ordinary speech and in nontechnical literature, the word *modulation* is imbued with various shades of meaning. From these, the suggestion of change is common to a number of similar conotations. Indeed, change is the implication most relevant to the process of modulation in electronics.

WHAT IS MODULATION?

Modulation imposes change; when one signal is modulated by another, the result is a composite signal. The basic objective of such modulation is best defined in terms of the practical accomplishment thereby gained. Most often, modulation implies the interaction between two signals in such a way that the information represented by one of them can be again recovered at a different time, or at a different place.

In this definition of modulation, the signal invested with the information is termed the *modulating signal* or, more simply, the *modulation*. The other signal is appropriately called the carrier. The "piggyback" relationship implied by such nomenclature is close to fact. In a very real sense, the modulation is transported on the carrier. The unique, but not necessarily obvious, consequence of such transport is the creation of a composite signal. This new signal is somewhat deceptively known as the *modulated carrier*. Fig. 1-1 shows the composite signal generated in a simple amplitude modulation. The new waveform is called the *amplitude-modulation pattern*. The interpretation of observable and partially concealed aspects of this graphic display will be shown to be of paramount importance to the achievement of desirable performance in equipments employing amplitude-modulation techniques.

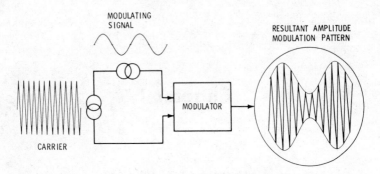

Fig. 1-1. Amplitude modulation resulting from interaction of two frequencies.

The waveforms shown in Fig. 1-2A and Fig. 1-2B have superficial resemblances to the amplitude-modulation pattern. Yet, these waveforms do not represent modulation. Analytically, they do not qualify because new frequencies are not generated. Practically, they will not behave in the manner of modulated carriers. Although

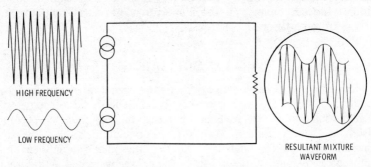

(A) Large-signal, high-frequency waveform mixed with small-signal, low-frequency waveform.

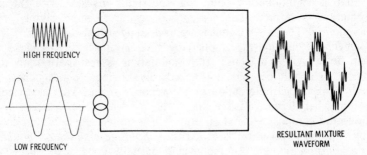

(B) Small-signal, high-frequency waveform mixed with large-signal, low-frequency waveform.

Fig. 1-2. Mixture of two frequencies.

useful information may reside in one of the paired waves, the other serves no useful function. Combinations such as these are simple mixtures of frequencies. Mixture waves are to be found prior to modulation and subsequent to demodulation.

WHY MODULATE?

The human voice is readily converted by a microphone into audio-frequency currents. Such currents are capable of being reproduced as sound waves by a distant receiver at the opposite end of a wire line. Such transmission of information is effected without the complexities and costs of modulation. This being the case, it is only natural to ask, "Why modulate?"

A close scrutiny is needed to account for the widespread use of modulation in all phases of the communications art. Consider a simple wire telephone system as shown in Fig. 1-3A in which voice frequencies, from 300 cps to 3000 cps, are transmitted. How many simultaneous telephone conversations could such a simple system support? Sadly, the existence of more than a single conversation at a time would produce confusion in the receiver. Increasing the number of wires would offer no practical solution. It would soon

(A) Voice-frequency transmission allows operation of only one channel.

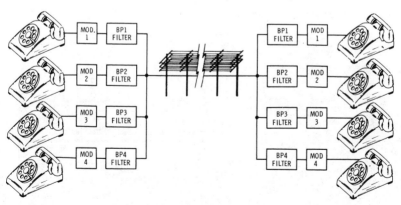

(B) Modulation techniques enables many-channel operation.

Fig. 1-3. Modulation makes telephony practical.

be found that the total weight of such multiple cable could not be supported by the familiar telephone pole. Moreover, the cost of the required toll-station equipment would be passed on to the user, making the residential telephone a status symbol.

Modulation provides a relatively simple and highly effective solution. Instead of impressing voice frequencies directly on the line, they are instead employed to modulate a relatively high frequency oscillation. The signal then sent over the wire could be 50 kc, rather than in the 300-cps to 3000-cps range. Then other modulated carriers can be simultaneously sent over the line. For example, a second such signal could be in the vicinity of 45 kc. Similarly, a third could be in the vicinity of 55 kc. Additional modulated carriers could be impressed on the line. Each modulated carrier would exist on the line independently of all other. At any receiving station, the frequency discrimination imposed by appropriate selective filters permits only the desired modulated carrier to reach the demodulator and receiver. Thus, modulation in conjunction with frequency-selective filters allows the use of a single wire pair to carry many simultaneous conversations without interferences at the receiving end as shown in Fig. 1-3B.

Although one conversation at a time could be accomplished with a simple wire system without modulation, the situation encountered in radio is even more ominous. Electromagnetic oscillations at voice frequencies show relatively little inclination to radiate into space without the assistance of impractical, extensive antenna installations and tremendously high power levels. Such a transmitting station would indeed dominate the landscape as we see in Fig. 1-4. It becomes logical, for these reasons, to merge the lower frequency

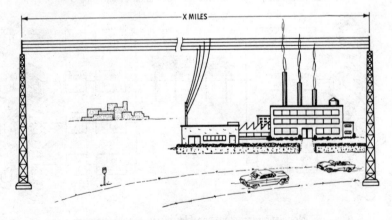

Fig. 1-4. Radiotelephony without modulation would require uneconomical power levels and large antennas.

information-bearing signal with the high-frequency propagating signal. Such a merger, or modulation, begets a modulated carrier with the useful features of both components. Additionally, through the use of frequency selectivity at the receiver, the modulating process pays the same dividends described for wire telephony. Many stations can be on the air simultaneously, and reception can be limited to any particular one of them. Thus, radio, as we know it today, is at the very outset dependent on modulation.

Here, it is appropriate to again contemplate the mixture waveforms of Fig. 1-2A and Fig. 1-2B. The high-frequency signal represented in these waveforms would propagate into space from appropriate antenna. They would not, however, carry along with them the information represented by the low-frequency waves. Such waveforms do not behave as modulated carriers. Note that despite the disturbances created by the presence of the low-frequency waves, the cycle-to-cycle amplitudes of the high-frequency waves remain constant. In other words, amplitude modulation does not exist in these composite waveforms.

WHAT IS AMPLITUDE MODULATION?

In amplitude modulation the envelope of the carrier is varied by the modulating signal. Changes in the amplitude of the modulating signal produce corresponding changes in carrier amplitude. Changes in the frequency of the modulating signal produce corresponding changes in the frequency of the signal superimposed on the carrier envelope. An apparently simple kind of amplitude modulation is found in radiotelegraphy. Here, the dots and dashes are formed by interrupting or chopping the carrier signal. Modulation by chopping is simple only in the sense that the technique is brought about by nothing more than the actuation of a switch, as shown in Fig. 1-5. Let it suffice for the moment to suppose that telegraphic code is not the simplest form of amplitude modulation. Nor is such an amplitude-modulated carrier as that depicted in Fig. 1-6 repre-

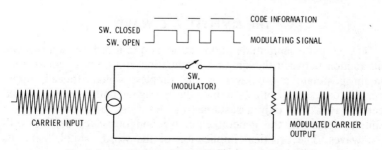

Fig. 1-5. Amplitude modulation by chopping carrier signal.

sentative of the simplest amplitude modulation.

These examples of amplitude modulation help us to recognize basic features which pertain to amplitude modulation in general. In order to gain insight into more than superficial features of such general examples of amplitude modulation, we must seek out a particular amplitude modulation which is truly the simplest of all possibilities. Such an amplitude modulation will then serve as the building block from which we can understand the behavior of more complex amplitude modulations. This study method is important because amplitude modulation is accompanied by other phenomena.

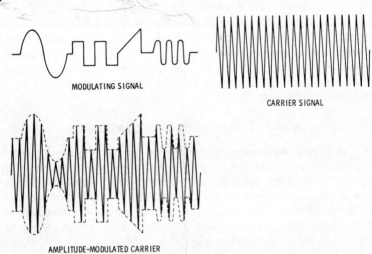

MODULATING SIGNAL

CARRIER SIGNAL

AMPLITUDE-MODULATED CARRIER

Fig. 1-6. Example of complex amplitude modulation.

Let us now explore concepts which can lead us to a form of amplitude modulation which, from both mathematical and practical considerations, will serve as the simplest type which can be produced.

THE SIMPLEST A-C WAVE

The simplest amplitude modulation is produced by appropriate interaction between the simplest modulation and carrier signals. One might postulate a d-c level as the simplest signal. Indeed, direct current can serve both as a modulating signal and as a modulated carrier. However, only a sustained d-c level can be considered as a simple signal. In the general case, we find ourselves dealing with a-c waves. The practical implication of the word "simple" and its significance will now be shown.

12

The so-called sine wave is the simplest a-c wave. The graphical generation of the sine wave is shown in Fig. 1-7. The sine wave of voltage can be expressed mathematically:

$$e = E \sin \omega t$$
$$= E \sin \theta$$

where,

e is the instantaneous value of voltage at time t,
E is the peak voltage,
ω is $2\pi f$ (expressed in radians),
f is the frequency in cycles per second,
t is time in seconds,
θ is the angle in degrees (θ is equal to ωt).

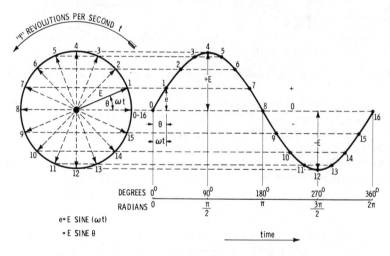

Fig. 1-7. Graphical generation of one cycle of a sine wave.

A relationship exists between f and t:

$$f = \frac{1}{t} \quad \text{and} \quad t = \frac{1}{f}$$

where,

f is the frequency in cycles per second,
t is the length of one period of frequency f, in seconds.

It is not at all obvious why the sine wave qualifies as the simplest a-c wave. Why not semicircular waves, or esthetically formed hyperbolic waves? Again, it might appear that no wave could be simpler than a rectangular wave.

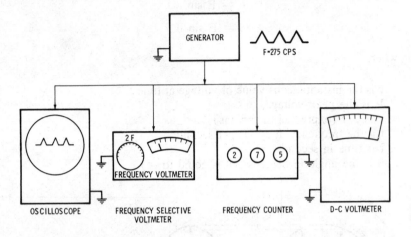

Fig. 1-8. Experiment investigating frequency components of waves.

Such "intuition" would be quickly refuted by the experimental investigation depicted in Fig. 1-8. Here, the pulse repetition rate of a sawtooth wave of 275 cps is indicated by the oscilloscope and, more accurately, by the frequency counter. The frequency-selective voltmeter reveals that this is not the whole picture, however. If we represent the pulse repetition rate by f, we find that considerable energy is invested in whole number multitudes of f. The frequency selective voltmeter shows the presence of various amplitudes of frequencies at $2f$, $3f$, $4f$, $5f$, etc. The d-c voltmeter deflects indicating a d-c component present.

However, when we apply a sine wave to these instruments, the results are different. Significantly the sine wave is free of these "hidden" frequencies. A sine wave which repeats itself f times per second gives a true representation of itself on the oscilloscope and on the digital counter. The only response detected on the frequency-selective voltmeter is f itself. Also, the d-c voltmeter will not deflect, indicating that there is a lack of any d-c component in the sine wave.

THE FOURIER THEOREM

Interpretation of the experimental evidence gained from the experiment of Fig. 1-8 leads to the *Fourier Theorem*. According to this theorem, all waveforms may be resolved into harmonically related sine waves. The sine wave is the "building block" of all waveforms. "Harmonic relationship" implies sine-wave frequencies related to a lowest frequency by whole-number multiples. The lowest frequency is known as the *fundamental* frequency. The fundamental frequency is the *first harmonic*. The fundamental frequency is responsible for the pulse repetition rate of the waveform. Depending on the shape of the waveform, there are various amounts of frequencies twice (second harmonic), three times (third harmonic), four times (fourth harmonic), five times (fifth harmonic), and of higher multiples of the fundamental frequency. As a consequence of the particular harmonics present and of their phase relationships, there is often a resultant d-c level. The d-c level, if present, corresponds to zero frequency. Frequencies that are lower than the fundamental (subharmonics) are not involved. Also, there are no fractional subharmonic or harmonic frequencies. All harmonic frequencies are sine waves.

The Fourier Theorem will be shown to have two important bearings on the study of amplitude modulation. In the first place, the Fourier composition of pulse waveforms provides an instructive setting for the appreciation of the true nature of amplitude-modulated waves. This is because both pulse waveforms (nonsinusoidal waves) and amplitude modulated waves are *composite* waves. In both instances the composition is more involved that it appears. The oscilloscope display of the amplitude-modulated wave reveals that the amplitude of the carrier frequency is varying at a frequency and an amplitude determined by the modulation. As will be shown, this is not the true picture of the frequency spectrum. Secondly, it is already obvious that modulation by a pulse waveform involves modulation by several, or many, frequencies. Appropriately, then, let us explore or review some of the results of the Fourier Theorem itself.

How Harmonics Produce Pulse Waveforms

The combining of harmonically related sine waves to produce various pulse waveforms is shown in Figs. 1-9, 1-10, and 1-11. The resultant waveform is shaped by three factors. These are the *number* of harmonics present, their *amplitudes,* and their relative *phase* displacements. The phase of a harmonic is referred to some arbitrary zero time. It is not meaningful to compare the phases of waves having nonharmonically related frequencies. Networks containing reactive elements can change the shape of pulse waveforms because both the relative amplitudes and the phase displacements of the harmonics can be thereby changed. The sine wave itself is unique in that its shape cannot be altered by any linear network. Conver-

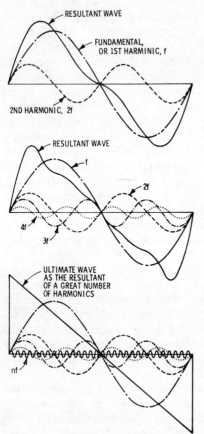

RESULTANT WAVE

FUNDAMENTAL, OR 1ST HARMINIC, f

2ND HARMONIC, 2f

RESULTANT WAVE

f

2f

4f

3f

ULTIMATE WAVE AS THE RESULTANT OF A GREAT NUMBER OF HARMONICS

nf

Fig. 1-9. The harmonic content of a nonsinusoidal waveform (sawtooth).

sion of a sine wave to a nonsinusoidal wave is always the consequence of nonlinearity. A nonlinear device diverts energy from the fundamental into higher harmonics.

In principle, many waveforms require an infinite number of harmonics. In practice, several (ten) harmonics often suffice. This follows from the fact that the general tendency is for diminishing energy content in the higher harmonics. The essential features of the waveform are for this reason established by the fundamental and a relatively few harmonics. In digital pulse work and in techniques requiring precise timing intervals, the faithful reproduction and preservation of waves with fast rise times is important. In such instances, the qualifying phrase "relatively few" might signify considerably more than ten harmonics. Figs. 1-12 and 1-13 are instructive in this regard. Fig. 1-12 illustrates this very effectively. Consider the condition where D is 50 microseconds (μsec) and R is 500 microseconds.

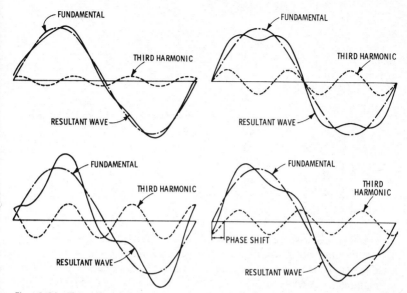

Fig. 1-10. The effect of changing the amplitude of a harmonic in a nonsinusoidal waveform.

Fig. 1-11. The effect of shifting the phase relations of a harmonic in a nonsinusoidal waveform.

Then δ is equal to 0.1, and y is 0 when n is 10, 20, 30, etc. This indicates that the harmonic content of the waveform from 0 to 1/δ includes the first ten harmonics (n=10). Now, as D (pulse width) decreases or as R (period) increases, δ becomes smaller and n becomes larger, indicating that the number of harmonics from 0 to 1/δ increases beyond ten.

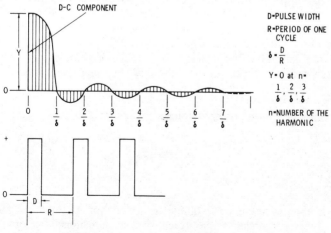

Fig. 1-12. Harmonic content of narrow, rectangular, unidirectional pulses.

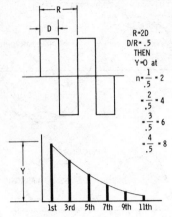

R=2D
D/R=.5
THEN
Y=0 at
$n = \frac{1}{.5} = 2$
$\frac{2}{.5} = 4$
$\frac{3}{.5} = 6$
$\frac{4}{.5} = 8$

Fig. 1-13. Main harmonic frequencies of rectangular waveform with a 50-percent duty cycle.

1st 3rd 5th 7th 9th 11th

Fig. 1-13 is a special case of the rectangular pulse. Here we have a rectangular pulse that has a 50-percent *duty cycle*. This is the case when R is twice as long as D , or D/R is equal to 0.5. Then, y is equal to 0 when n is 2, $(1/\delta = 1/.5), 4, (2/\delta = 2/.5)$, etc. Thus, the harmonic content of this waveform consists of the odd harmonics of the basic frequency.

In a waveform consisting only of odd harmonics, no d-c component can exist. In general, the inclusion of even harmonics brings about the appearance of the d-c component. It is possible, however, to have phase conditions of even harmonics such that no d-c component will result. The d-c component is the consequence of some nonsymmetrical distribution of area in the waveform.

Nonsinusoidal or pulse waveforms can be synthesized in a linear circuit by applying a number of harmonically related waves. Such pulses are mixture waveforms in which the involved frequencies are phase-synchronized to the lowest frequency present. Conversely, nonlinearity can disperse the energy of a single-frequency sine wave into harmonic frequencies. Again, the harmonics combine to form a fixed waveform due to their inherent phase synchronization.

The Fourier Theorem

A simplified form of the Fourier Theorem follows:

$$e = C + A_1 \sin (\omega_1 t) + A_2 \sin (\omega_2 t) + A_3 \sin (\omega_3 t) + \ldots + A_n \sin (\omega_n t)$$

where,

e   is the instantaneous voltage as a function of time, t. Therefore, e represents the trace of the nonsinusoidal or pulse waveform.

C is the d-c component,
A_1 is the peak amplitude of the first harmonic, or fundamental,
A_2 is the peak amplitude of the second harmonic,
A_3 is the peak amplitude of the third harmonic,
A_n represents the peak amplitude of the nth harmonic,
ω_1 is $2\pi f$,
ω_2 is $4\pi f$,
ω_3 is $6\pi f$,
ω_n is $n2\pi f$,
f is the fundamental frequency.

In order to make this equation more descriptive, the *phase* of each harmonic can be indicated; thus:

$$e = C + A_1 \sin (\omega_1 t + \theta_1) + A_2 \sin (\omega_2 t + \theta_2) + \ldots$$

where,

θ_1 represents the phase displacement of the fundamental frequency relative to an arbitrary zero time. Usually, the start of the fundamental wave establishes this zero time.

θ_2 represents the phase displacement of the second harmonic relative to the above chosen zero time, and the same reasoning is applied to θ_3, θ_4, θ_5, . . . θ_n.

C will be zero or will have some finite value depending on the amplitudes and the phases of the harmonics making up the wave.

THE SIMPLEST AMPLITUDE MODULATION

If the sine wave is the simplest a-c wave, it should follow that the simplest kind of amplitude modulation is that due to the interaction of a sine-wave modulating signal and a sine-wave carrier signal. This is indeed the case, although we should further qualify this statement by restricting the interaction to that produced in a linear modulator. This means that our sine waves suffer no distortion other than that required for the basic modulation function itself.

It might appear that undue concern has been given our search for the simplest type of amplitude modulation. It will shortly become evident why this search leads to the true nature of amplitude modulation. Already it can be appreciated that sinewave modulation of a sine-wave carrier in a linear modulator must be the least complex modulation by virtue of the involvement of *single* frequencies in both modulation and carrier signals. This has been shown to be the consequence of the Fourier Theorem. Thus, the otherwise "simple" amplitude modulation produced in radiotelegraphy involves a rectangular modulating wave in the production of dots and dashes. This is the equivalent of several to many simultaneous modulating signals, depending on how many harmonics of the code speed we decide are essential for faithful reproduction. We are now ready to investigate the important practical implications of simple as well as the more generally encountered complex types of amplitude modulation.

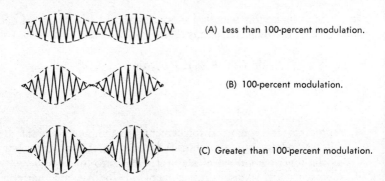

(A) Less than 100-percent modulation.

(B) 100-percent modulation.

(C) Greater than 100-percent modulation.

Fig. 1-14. Amplitude modulated waveforms.

Fig. 1-14A and Fig. 1-14B show simple amplitude-modulation patterns. They represent the kind of sine-wave interaction described above. In Fig. 1-14A the modulation is relatively shallow. In Fig. 1-14B the modulation is complete. Both of these modulations are capable of conveying the modulating information with no distortion or extraneous effects. This is not true of the pattern shown in Fig. 1-14C. Here the strength of the modulating signal is greater than that needed to just bring the carrier to zero level. It is evident that the envelope of the modulating signal is no longer sinusoidal. It can be seen that the information borne by this pattern is something other than that corresponding to a sine-wave modulating signal.

Graphical Generation of Amplitude-Modulation Pattern

Fig. 1-15 shows the graphical generation of an amplitude-modulation pattern. The basic mechanism of generation is similar to that depicted in Fig. 1-7 for the generation of the simple sine wave. In this case, however, the rotating vector has *two* variations. As before, the rotation proceeds at the angular velocity corresponding to the frequency of the carrier wave. Superimposed on this rotation is a variation in amplitude corresponding to the sine-wave modulating signal. The variation in amplitude is represented by a periodic change in *length* of the rotating vector. The cyclic change in the length of the vector has the rate which corresponds to the frequency of the modulating signal. Keep in mind that the carrier vector makes *many* complete revolutions per revolution of the modulating-signal vector. This derives from the general situation wherein the carrier frequency is much higher than that of the modulation.

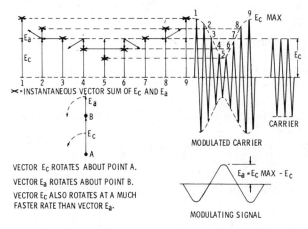

Fig. 1-15. Graphical generation of an amplitude-modulated waveform.

In Fig. 1-15, the peaks of the individual carrier cycles constitute the waveform of the modulation envelope. These peaks are generated only when the rotating vector (E_c) passes through its vertical position. When the rotating vector is in any other graphical position, it generates portions of the carrier cycles other than their peaks.

The presentation of the amplitude-modulation pattern by the representation of Fig. 1-15 is instructive, but it ignores a basic fact pertaining to amplitude modulation. We will increase our viewing range through interpretation of the equation which mathematically describes amplitude modulation. It will not be necessary to rely on the mathematical analysis for appreciation of these facts, however. We will subsequently modify the graphical generator in order to bring out the same facts.

WHAT THE AMPLITUDE-MODULATION EQUATION TELLS US

Two sine waves interact in a linear modulator. One of these waves has a frequency many times that of the other. This wave will be the carrier signal. The lower-frequency wave is the modulating signal. The peak amplitude of the modulating signal must not exceed the peak amplitude of the carrier signal in order to avoid overmodulation. Using standard sine-wave notation, the expressions for these two waves may be written as follows:

$$e_c = E_c \sin \omega_c t \text{ for the carrier signal}$$

$$e_a = E_a \sin \omega_a t \text{ for the modulating signal}$$

where,

e_c = the instantaneous value of the carrier voltage (in volts) at time t,

E_c = the peak value of the carrier voltage (in volts),

ω_c = $2\pi f$ at the frequency f of the carrier,

t = time in seconds,

e_a = the instantaneous value of the modulating-signal voltage (in volts),

E_a = the peak value of the modulating-signal voltage (in volts),

ω_a = $2\pi f$ at the frequency f of the modulating voltage.

It is only reasonable to expect that the equation for the interaction of these two signals must take into account the relative amounts present. For this purpose the ratio of the modulating-signal amplitude (E_a) to that of the carrier amplitude (E_c) is a useful quantity. The ratio is most simply expressed in terms of the peak amplitudes and is indicated by *m*. That is,

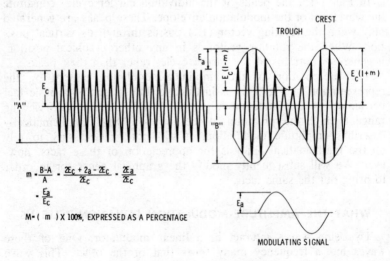

$$m = \frac{B-A}{A} = \frac{2E_c + 2a - 2E_c}{2E_c} = \frac{2E_a}{2E_c}$$

$$= \frac{E_a}{E_c}$$

$M = (\ m\ ) \times 100\%$, EXPRESSED AS A PERCENTAGE

MODULATING SIGNAL

Fig. 1-16. Modulation factor m and M.

$$m = \frac{E_a}{E_c}$$

The term m is known as the *modulation factor*. It is often expressed as a percentage M. Fig. 1-16 shows this graphically.

The basic nature of the modulating interaction is that the multiplication product of the carrier and modulating signals is added to the carrier. The mathematical expression of this fact is

$$e = E_c \sin \omega_c t + m(E_c \sin \omega_c t)(\sin \omega_a t)$$

where,

   e = the instantaneous value of the modulated wave.

By the method of trigonometric identities, this expression can be written in a different form. This will now be done without recourse to explanation of the mathematical details. The significance of the transformation will become obvious to the reader whether or not he possesses the relevant background in mathematics.

The modified (but equivalent) equation is

$$e = E_c \sin (\omega_c t) + \frac{mE_c}{2} \sin (\omega_c + \omega_a)t + \frac{mE_c}{2} \sin (\omega_c - \omega_a)t$$

Three terms are involved in this expression. The terms are separated by the addition signs. Recall, first, that the equation defines the instantaneous value of e as a function of time, t. The entire right-hand side of the equation will tell us what kind of signals are actually contained in the amplitude-modulation pattern described by the trace of e.

The first term we recognize immediately as the original value of the carrier signal. It is present in unaltered form despite the fact that it is also involved in an interaction with the modulating signal.

The second term is a wave with frequency equal to the *sum of the carrier frequency and the modulation frequency*. Its amplitude is dependent on the modulation factor, m. Thus, if m is 1, the amplitude of this term is one-half that of the carrier; m = 1 corresponds to complete, or 100-percent modulation. We see here the production of a frequency component different from either carrier or modulating signals.

The third term is a wave with frequency equal to the *difference between carrier and modulating frequencies*. Its amplitude has the same dependency on m as does the second term.

The second term is called the *upper sideband*. The third term is called the *lower sideband*. Thus the modulated wave consists of the carrier, the upper sideband, and the lower sideband. The modulating signal is *not* included. This is shown in Fig. 1-17. Note that

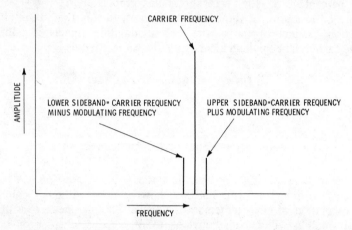

Fig. 1-17. Frequency spectrum with a single-frequency, sine-wave, modulating signal.

when m is zero, the sidebands disappear. In other words, no modulation is present and we have only the first term, the carrier. All circuit designs and operating adjustments pertaining to amplitude modulation must be carried out with due allowance made for these three frequency-components in the modulated wave.

Graphical Indication of the Sidebands

The equation of amplitude modulation points out the existence of the sideband frequencies. This mathematical analysis is readily verified by experiments with bandpass filters and is shown in Fig. 1-18, yet there appears to be no evidence of the the sideband frequencies in the graphical generation of the amplitude-modulation pattern of Fig. 1-15. In all honesty, it must be said that the discovery of sidebands by purely graphical means would not be likely in the absence of information from other sources. The length-varying vector of Fig. 1-15 generates the amplitude-modulation pattern in the course of its rotation. Where are the sidebands?

Interestingly, Fig. 1-15 may be modified to show the existence of sidebands. Fig. 1-19 is similar to Fig. 1-15. However, the length-varying vector is now depicted as the resultant of two added vectors. The two added vectors represent the sideband frequencies. They rotate in the same direction as the carrier, but at different speeds. The one which represents the upper sideband rotates at a faster speed than the carrier vector. This corresponds with the

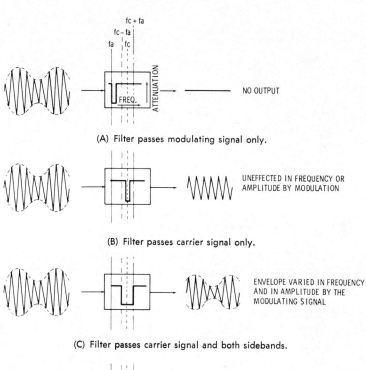

(A) Filter passes modulating signal only.

(B) Filter passes carrier signal only.

(C) Filter passes carrier signal and both sidebands.

(D) Filter passes carrier signal but offers some attenuation to the sidebands.

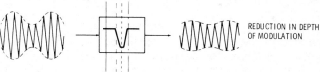

(E) Filter passes upper sideband.

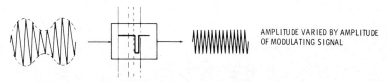

(F) Filter passes lower sideband.

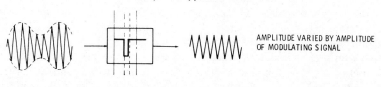

Fig. 1-18. Effects of bandpass filtering on amplitude-modulated waveform.

25

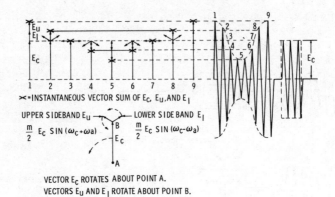

VECTOR E_c ROTATES ABOUT POINT A.
VECTORS E_u AND E_l ROTATE ABOUT POINT B.

Fig. 1-19. Generating amplitude-modulated waveform with rotating vectors representing the sidebands.

fact that the frequency of the upper sideband is greater than the carrier frequency. The upper-sideband frequency is the sum of the carrier and the modulation frequencies.

The other added vector represents the lower sideband. Accordingly, its rotation is depicted as slower than that of the carrier vector. This corresponds to the fact that the frequency of the lower sideband is less than the carrier frequency. The lower sideband frequency is the difference between the carrier and modulation frequencies.

We see that the modification introduced in Fig. 1-19 brings the graphical generation of the amplitude-modulated wave into harmony with the facts derived from both mathematics and measurement. We have three methods of dealing with the relation of carrier and sideband components of the amplitude-modulated wave. Mathematical analysis, experimental investigation, and graphical representation concur on the nature of amplitude modulation.

Complex Amplitude Modulation

Most often, amplitude modulation involves a more complex interaction than that due to two sine waves. Usually the carrier is a sine wave, but the modulating signal is made up of *several* or many frequencies. These multiple frequencies may originate from separate sources. Alternately, they may originate from a single nonsinusoidal source. In the first instance, one can conjure the ideal situation of a band of musical instruments, where each emits its unique range of sine-wave tones. Of course, actual musical instruments produce sounds rich in harmonic overtones. This leads us to the second case where the harmonics from a single nonsinusoidal source are simultaneously impressed on the carrier. Many modulations are mixtures of these two cases. That is, more than one modulating-signal source is involved, and each source is accompanied by harmonics. In any event, it is clear that the carrier will undergo modulation by each sine wave interacting with it. The result is a simple extention of the simple modulation mechanism revealed by the amplitude-modulation equation. Each sine-wave component of the modulating signal(s) will generate its pair of sidebands. It will do this as if it were the only sine-wave modulation present.

We see, as a consequence of the Fourier Theorem and the amplitude-modulation equation, that complex modulation involves many sideband frequencies. This is illustrated in the modulations de-

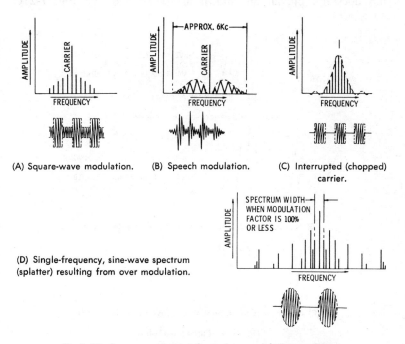

(A) Square-wave modulation.   (B) Speech modulation.   (C) Interrupted (chopped) carrier.

(D) Single-frequency, sine-wave spectrum (splatter) resulting from over modulation.

Fig. 1-20. Frequency spectrum for various modulating conditions.

picted in Fig. 1-20. Note that over-modulation by a sine wave likewise produces numerous sidebands. These extend far beyond the bandwidth required for 100-percent modulation. This is a reasonable occurrence in light of the fact that the modulation envelope is no longer a sine wave. The production of such extraneous sidebands is to be avoided in all communications techniques. Its occurrence is known as *splatter*. The consequences are interference with other stations and distortion of its own modulating information.

CARRIER-LEVEL SHIFT

In a sine-wave—modulated carrier, the resultant amplitude-modulation pattern is symmetrical in the sense that the average envelope amplitude is equal to the amplitude of the carrier prior to modulation. This is shown in Fig. 1-21A. It should be kept in mind that amplitude, not power, values are presently under discussion. The conditions depicted in Fig. 1-21A can exist only when the modulating characteristics of the device or amplifier involved is linear. Such modulating linearity corresponds to the situation in which the amplitude of the modulated wave is directly proportional to the amplitude of the modulating wave. Situations where this relationship does not prevail are shown in Fig. 1-21B and Fig. 1-21C.

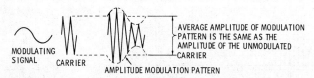

(A) Linear modulation—no carrier-level shift.

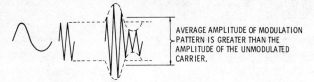

(B) Nonlinear modulation with positive carrier-level shift.

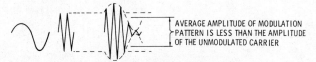

(C) Nonlinear modulation with negative carrier-level shift.

Fig. 1-21. Carrier-level shift.

In these cases the average amplitude of the modulated carrier envelope differs from the amplitude of the carrier prior to modulation. Hence, these situations are designated as carrier-level shift. The carrier-level shift of Fig. 1-21B is appropriately described as positive, whereas that of Fig. 1-21C is described as negative.

Obviously, carrier-level shift involves distortion. Positive carrier-level shift is not too detrimental to speech intelligibility. Accordingly, positive carrier-level shift is sometimes employed to provide a modulating factor in excess of 100 percent in the upward direction. This increases the "talk power" in some communications equipment. Negative carrier-level shift can produce disasterous results by causing overmodulation in the downward direction. Such overmodulation produces severe distortion and generates splatter which interferes with other stations. The presence of negative carrier-level shift in most instances reduces the talk power of a transmitter. When excessive, it causes the undesired modulating mode known as *downward modulation.* In downward modulation, the average power of the modulated wave is decreased during modulation. An antenna ammeter would show a decrease in current during modulation for such operation.

Two important facts must be recognized for a clear understanding of carrier-level shift. First, the modulation pattern of Fig. 1-21A does represent an increase in average power over the unmodulated carrier. This often is a stumbling block because it might seem contradictory to the lack of change in the average amplitude. ("Average" is given relative to a complete cycle of sine-wave modulation. The apparent discrepancy is resolved by recalling that power is proportional to the square of voltage or current. This makes the power in the outward excursion of the modulation pattern exceed the power in the inward excursion.)

The second fact of importance relevant to carrier-level shift is that the modulation patterns of B and C in Fig. 1-21 do not imply carrier-level shift unless the modulating signal is sinusoidal. It could very well be that the envelope convolutions of these modulation patterns result from faithful modulation by modulating waves of like shape. Indeed, during speech modulation the modulating conditions correspond much more to the patterns of B and C than of A in Fig. 1-21. If, however, the equipment passes the test provisions of A, it can be safely concluded that no carrier-level shift is inflicted by the modulated amplifier itself.

In testing for carrier-level shift, an oscilloscope is not always essential. A quick indication of carrier-level shift is obtained when, with sine-wave modulation, a change is produced in the d-c plate current of the modulated amplifier. However, speech modulation due to its inherent lack of waveform symmetry can produce d-c plate-current fluctuations, with perfectly linear modulation.

DEMODULATION

Demodulation, or *detection,* is the inverse of modulation. In the demodulation process, the original modulating signal is recovered from the amplitude-modulated wave. Demodulation is an extensive subject. Its inclusion here is limited to the extent that its discussion can be used to cast further illumination on amplitude modulation.

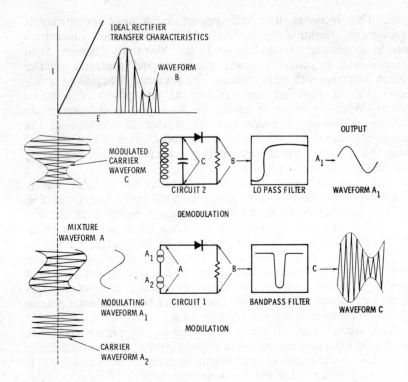

Fig. 1-22. A comparison of amplitude modulation and demodulation.

An interesting and instructive relationship between amplitude modulation and demodulation is shown in Fig. 1-22. Two experiments are depicted here. Both depend on the linear forward characteristic of an "ideal" rectifier. (The forward conduction relationship is linear, being represented by a straight line. The rectifier is a nonlinear device when considering *both* forward and reverse characteristics.)

First, we apply waveform A to circuit 1 in Fig. 1-22. This is a mixture wave consisting of a carrier frequency (A_2) and a lower modulating frequency (A_i). As a consequence of the rectification, waveform B is obtained. When this wave is passed through a bandpass filter with center frequency equal to that of the carrier, we obtain the amplitude-modulated wave, C.

Next, we apply waveform C to circuit 2 in Fig. 1-22. Waveform C is an amplitude-modulated wave. The consquence of rectification is identical to that of the first experiment, for we again produce waveform B. This time waveform B is passed through a low-pass filter which goes into its attenuation region at a frequency somewhat higher than the modulating frequency, but well below the carrier frequency. This time we obtain the original modulating signal A_1.

The first experiment yielded amplitude modulation. The second experiment provided amplitude demodulation. We see that the type of filtering accorded to waveform B is responsible for the different results in the two experiments. Often the role played by the nonlinear element is emphasized at the expense of the contribution of the subsequent filter network. These two experiments reveal that both circuit functions are important.

The ideal rectifier characteristic is the simplest transfer function to use for the purpose of illustrating the basic mechanism of demodulation. However, any nonlinear relationship between the

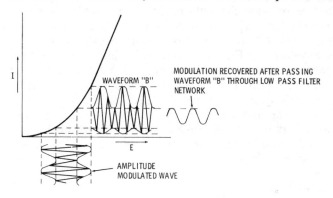

(A) Using the lower portion of a curve.

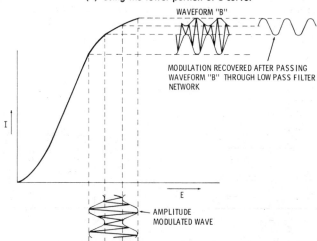

(B) Using the upper portion of a curve.

Fig. 1-23. Demodulation from nonlinear current-voltage characteristics.

voltage impressed across a device and the current through it will cause demodulation. Such demodulation may be intentional, as in the second detector of a superheterodyne radio. On the other hand, demodulation often is undesirable. For example, any nonlinearity in audio amplifier circuitry enables broadcasting stations to produce interference. Hearing aids are often plagued by such inadvertent detection. Fig. 1-23 shows demodulations of more general occurrence than that of Fig. 1-22. We can conclude that any type B waveform is a candidate for either modulation or demodulation, depending on subsequent filtering.

The basic characteristic of such waveforms is that they display a change in symmetry between top and bottom undulations. In the absence of additional information there would be no way of knowing whether such waveforms were produced by "modulators" or "demodulators." However, it is evident that the composite waves (the B waveforms of Figs. 1-22 and 1-23) differ from the symmetrical amplitude patterns previously discussed. Instead of linear modulation, we now encounter nonlinear modulation. This will be discussed more in detail in Chapter 3. It will suffice here to recognize that both linear and nonlinear modulation produce the same results at the output of a bandpass filter. Demodulation, on the other hand, requires a change in symmetry of the modulation envelope prior to filtering.

Detector Circuits

Figs. 1-24 and 1-25 are representative detector circuits commonly employed for demodulation of amplitude-modulated waves. Simple half-wave and full-wave diode detector circuits are shown in Fig. 1-24. Low-pass filtering at the output is provided by capaci-

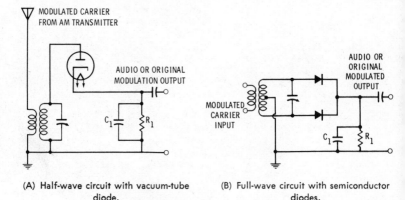

(A) Half-wave circuit with vacuum-tube diode.

(B) Full-wave circuit with semiconductor diodes.

Fig. 1-24. Simple diode detector circuits.

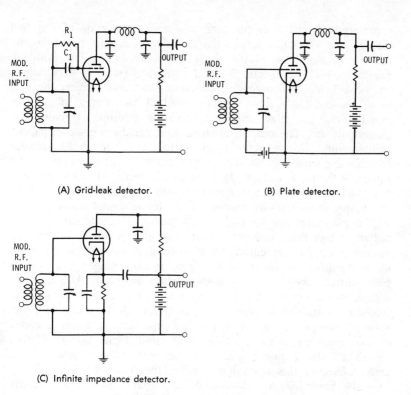

(A) Grid-leak detector.

(B) Plate detector.

(C) Infinite impedance detector.

Fig. 1-25. Vacuum-tube detector circuits.

tor C1 shunted across load resistance R1. Such filtering is generally quite satisfactory due to the great disparity between carrier and
modulating frequencies usually encountered. Diode detector cir-
uits exert a loading effect on the parallel tuned tank, thereby lower-
ing its Q and degrading frequency selectivity. The full-wave circuit
is less troublesome in this respect than the simpler half-wave configuration. Moreover, the full-wave circuit can provide greater
detection efficiency due to the fact that both halves of the carrier
cycle contribute to the output. Both circuits approach the linear
detection mode depicted in Fig. 1-22 for large input signals.

Vacuum-tube detector circuits are shown in Fig. 1-25. The circuit of Fig. 1-25A is the so-called grid-leak detector. This circuit
is approximately equivalent to a diode detector followed by a
directly coupled audio-amplifier stage. However, the requirements
for optimum demodulation efficiency and good amplifier performance tend to be antagonistic. In the absence of a signal, the tube
operates with zero bias. A radio-frequency carrier developed across
the tuned circuit produces a negative grid bias. Any modulation

33

superimposed on the carrier then results in a variation of this grid bias. These variations follow the modulation superimposed on the radio-frequency carrier (the modulation envelope). The grid-leak resistance (R1) prevents the grid capacitor (C1) from retaining the peak value of charge. Such a condition would subject the grid to a near-constant negative bias instead of bias which follows the modulation. The plate circuit reproduces grid-bias variations in amplified form. The output low-pass filter can be a choke-capacitor combination. This detector tends to follow a square-law transfer function for small signals. The output current is proportional to the square of the input voltage. This detector is useful when so operated, but produces considerable distortion with large input signals. Like the simple diode circuits, loading of the tuned circuit occurs.

The plate detector of Fig. 1-25B performs demodulation in its output, rather than its input circuit. The grid is biased to approximately plate current cutoff. Plate current flows only in response to the positive excursions of the input signal voltage. The average plate current then follows the modulation envelope. Although not a rigorous analogy, we have the approximate equivalent of a radio-frequency amplifier followed by a rectifying diode detector. From another viewpoint, the plate detector operates as a single-ended class-B amplifier stage. Providing the input signal is not allowed to exceed the negative grid bias, no grid current flows. As a consequence of this operational mode, the plate detector will not load the tuned circuit. Sharp-cutoff type pentodes are particularly suitable for operation as plate detectors.

The infinite-impedance detector of Fig. 1-25C operates as a nonlinear cathode follower. The cathode resistance maintains the grid to cathode voltage negative even in the presence of large input signals. Thus, this detector is also free from tuned circuit loading. Demodulation is accomplished by rectification in the grid-cathode circuit. If the plate circuit is opened, operation would continue with the grid-cathode circuit functioning as a diode. However, under this condition, there would be loading of the tuned circuit and there would be no current amplification developed across the cathode resistance. The cathode resistance is bypassed for carrier frequencies, but not for modulation frequencies. The tube therefore provides nearly 100-percent negative feedback for modulation frequencies. This results in a considerable decrease in output distortion compared to the other detector circuits described. The infinite-impedance detector operates as a linear demodulator over a wide range of input signal amplitude. 100-percent modulation can be handled without peak-clipping distortion.

Transistor counterparts can be made to simulate the operation of vacuum-tube detector circuits. In addition, the transistor uniquely

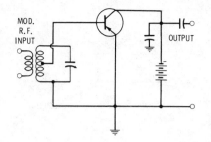

Fig. 1-26. Transistor detector circuit.

provides demodulation when its base-emitter input circuit is zero-biased and a large input signal is impressed. The circuit arrangement depicted in Fig. 1-26 is typical of the detector used in many small transistor radios. Detection occurs by rectification in the base-emitter diode. Subsequent amplification of the recovered modulation then takes place in the collector circuit. Although the transistor presents a much lower impedance to an associated resonant circuit than is ordinarily obtained with vacuum-tube detectors, degradation of Q can be avoided by a transformer step-down winding or an auto-transformer tap on the inductance.

Linear and Square-Law Detectors

A rectifying detector is considered "ideal" if it provides a linear relationship between impressed voltage and resultant current for one polarity only. A square-law detector is, for the sake of study, "ideal" if its relationship between impressed voltage and resultant current is a segment of a parabola. Such a curve is graphically produced by a current which is proportional to the square of the voltage. Analytically, these two basic detectors provide insights into demodulation resulting from any other nonlinearity. Detectors which are a combination of these two types, or which have more violent curves than depicted by the square law, can be understood by extention and extrapolation of the following fundamental features of the two types.

In Fig. 1-27A the spectrum of demodulation products is shown for the ideal rectifying or "linear" detector when exposed to a single-tone, sine-wave modulated carrier. Similarly, Fig. 1-27B shows the demodulation spectrum for a square-law detector. In both instances, the desired product is q, the modulating frequency. With the linear detector of Fig. 1-27A output filtering can be imposed to reject all demodulation products except q. This is possible even when the single-tone, sine-wave modulation is replaced by speech or music. In Fig. 1-27B, it is possible to select q and reject all other frequencies if the modulating signal is a single-tone sine wave. If, however, the modulating signal consists of the combined

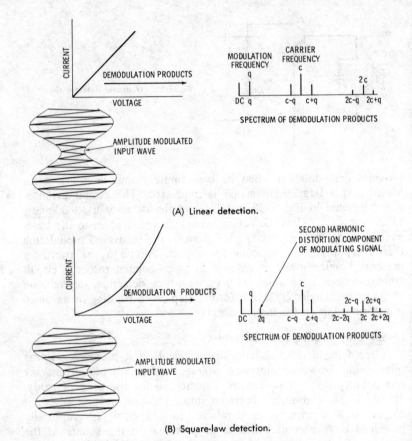

(A) Linear detection.

(B) Square-law detection.

Fig. 1-27. Frequency spectrum of basic detectors.

frequencies of speech or music, it is not possible to eliminate the second-harmonic distortion products represented by 2q. Thus, square-law detection distorts the original modulating information. This distortion reaches the high value of 25-percent when the modulation factor is one hundred percent. However, broadcasting stations modulate at an average level of about 40 percent, so the distortion accompanying square-law (or higher-order curvature) detection is considerably reduced. Also, in amateur and communications radio-telephone service, where higher modulating factors are strived for, speech fidelity suffers more than speech intelligibility. (Nonlinear detection is used in single-sideband reception. Here, the linear detector would not provide the required heterodyne action.)

Although the objective is to produce distortionless demodulation, detector circuits intended to nominally operate in their "linear" regions often perform similarly to square-law detectors when the input signal is either very weak or excessively strong. Also, square-law detection often finds favor in microwave and instrumentation applications.

INTERMODULATION AND CROSS MODULATION

The close relationship between modulation and demodulation is well exemplified by intermodulation and cross modulation. Both phenomena may be deliberately sought, or they may be inadvertently produced. Either may occur in "modulating" or "demodulating" circuits. The basic consequence of intermodulation is frequency translation. Sum and difference frequencies arise from the mutual action of two frequencies impressed on a nonlinear device. In essence, this is amplitude modulation. However, the output filter has different selectivity characteristics than would be the case in an amplitude-modulation process. In deliberate intermodulation the combining frequencies are rejected and only the sum or difference frequencies are passed. This is shown in Fig. 1-28A.

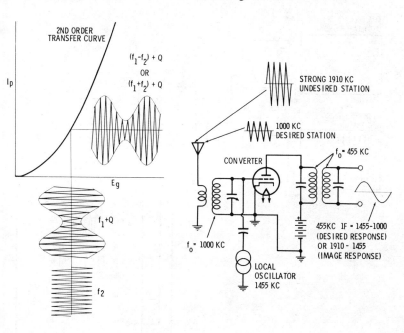

(A) Using the $I_p - E_g$ tube curve.   (B) As used in a superheterodyne receiver.

Fig. 1-28. Intermodulation.

The use of intermodulation is the basis of the superheterodyne radio receiver. The carrier of any station tuned in is frequency translated to a relatively low fixed frequency for subsequent amplification and ultimate demodulation. This is known as the *intermediate frequency*. The intermediate frequency (the intermodulation product) is the difference between the received frequency and the frequency generated by a local oscillator. A superheterodyne receiver may be designed to operate with the local-oscillator frequency displaced either below or above the frequency of the desired station. In any event, the oscillator frequency must be varied along with the input resonant circuit in order that the station frequency can mix with the oscillator frequency to produce the intermediate frequency.

Unfortunately, a station with its frequency removed from the desired station by twice the intermediate frequency can also intermodulate with the oscillator frequency to produce the intermediate frequency. This constitutes the so-called image response. Such interference can be greatly reduced by providing greater selectivity

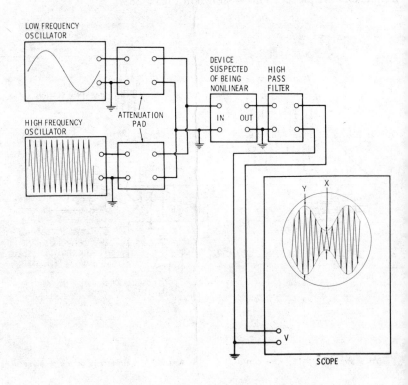

Fig. 1-29. Test for percentage of intermodulation.

prior to the converter stage. Fig. 1-28B shows a numerical example of desired and undesired intermodulation occurring in a superheterodyne receiver.

A commonly encountered instance of undesired intermodulation involves accoustical nonlinearity in speaker diaphragms. The presence of two or more exciting frequencies causes the generation of new frequencies which constitute very objectional distortion in sound reproduction systems.

A test setup for the measurement of percentage of intermodulation is shown in Fig. 1-29. High and low frequencies are impressed at the input of an amplifier or device suspected of being nonlinear and therefore capable of causing one input signal to modulate another. A high-pass filter is inserted between the output of the amplifier or device and the oscilloscope. This filter removes the low-frequency signal. This is necessary because the presence of the low-frequency signal would obscure the desired pattern. If there is intermodulation, an amplitude-modulation pattern will be seen with the high frequency modulated by the low frequency. As has been pointed out, such a pattern, even though it depicts the low frequency in its envelope, does *not* contain the low frequency as a separate component. This being the case, it is very important that the high-pass filter imparts high rejection to the low frequency. In order to bring this about, it is best that the cutoff frequency of the high-pass filter be not less than one-half of the frequency derived from the high-frequency oscillator. At the same time, the high-frequency oscillator should be at least ten times the frequency of the low-frequency oscillator. Although this rule is subject to considerable modification, depending on the characteristics of the filter, it nevertheless provides a good starting point in most practical situations.

Also, each oscillator should be isolated by at least 20 db of attenuation from the input terminals of the amplifier or device under test. This minimizes the effect of intermodulation which might occur within the test oscillators themselves. When only the high-frequency oscillatior is delivering a signal, the oscilloscope pattern should be a simple rendition of the high-frequency wave with no modulation envelope visible. When only the low-frequency oscillator is delivering a signal, the oscilloscope should display a straight line. If any low frequency is visible, attention must be given to the frequencies being employed for the test, and possibly to the filter. It should be ascertained that the input amplitudes of either high or low-frequency signals are not sufficient to overdrive or saturate the amplifier or device being tested. The percentage of intermodulation is obtained from the oscilloscope display by applying the formula:

$$\% \text{ Intermodulation} = \frac{Y - X}{Y + X} (100)$$

where,

X = the minimum instantaneous peak-to-peak voltage shown on the scope.

Y = the maximum instantaneous peak-to-peak voltage shown on the scope.

Cross modulation is the transfer of the modulating information from one carrier frequency to another. Once cross modulation has taken place within the radio-frequency input circuits of a radio receiver, no subsequent remedial measures are possible. The radio is, paradoxically, tuned to the right station but receives the wrong modulation. This phenomenon, like intermodulation, requires non-

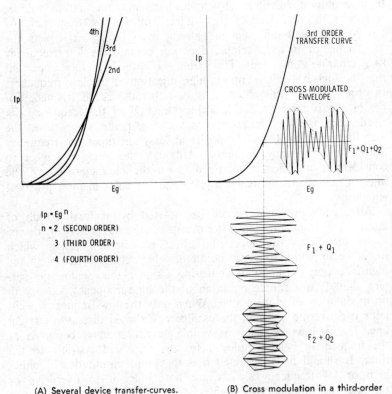

(A) Several device transfer-curves.

(B) Cross modulation in a third-order transfer curve.

Fig. 1-30. Cross modulation.

linearity for its occurrence. Fortunately, however, a more drastic nonlinearity is required for this aggravation. Whereas second-order curvature (Fig. 1-30A) of a device's transfer function suffices for demodulation and intermodulation, cross modulation can only happen if two stations encounter a transfer function with third order curvature or higher. Due to the need for automatic volume control in radios, the r-f stages generally operate in nonlinear grid-voltage versus plate current regions. This produces no harmful effects in the reception of a single station, for any inadvertent demodulation produced is removed by subsequent tuned circuits. Moreover, mild nonlinearity up to and including second-order or square-law relationship produces no envelope distortion of the modulated wave being amplified. Third-order curvature in the transfer function of the tube does produce trouble. Here, the modulation of one station is transferred to the carrier of the other station. See Fig. 1-30B.

Even when the selectivity of the tuned circuits attenuates an off-tune station sufficiently so that its modulation cannot reach the speaker by "normal" means, such a station can interfere by means of cross modulation. The most direct solution is the use of remote-cutoff tubes which have relatively gentle transfer curvatures and the use of high-selectivity LC circuits.

SUMMARY OF AMPLITUDE-MODULATION PRINCIPLES

1. Amplitude modulation produces a composite wave with the space propagating property of its high-frequency component and the information-conveying property of its low-frequency component.
2. The frequency spectrum of the modulated carrier no longer contains the modulating frequency. This spectrum is the natural consequence of any change in amplitude imparted to the envelope of a carrier frequency. The frequencies present in the spectra of the moduated carrier are:
   A. The carrier frequency.
   B. An upper-sideband frequency which is equal to the carrier frequency plus the modulating frequency.
   C. A lower-sideband frequency which is equal to the carrier frequency minus the carrier frequency minus the modulating frequency.
3. A pair of such sideband frequencies is generated for each frequency component of the modulating wave.
4. In ordinary amplitude modulation, power is added to the modulated carrier. The added power is equally distributed between the upper and lower sidebands.

5. The modulating information resides in the sidebands. This distribution of modulating information is redundant in the sense that a single sideband would suffice to convey the information. No modulating information is contained in the carrier frequency.

6. The carrier frequency serves the useful purpose of combining with the sideband frequencies to produce the modulation envelope. This modulation envelope is essential for the operation of the simple demodulators used in recovering the original modulating information. (Insofar as concerns the space propagating feature, this, as well as the modulating information, could be provided by a single sideband. Although this is a superior broadcasting technique, special attention is then required for demodulation).

7. In principle, amplitude modulation and demodulation produce similar results up to the point of filtering out undesired components.

8. Intermodulation, cross modulation, and frequency translation are processes closely akin to amplitude modulation. These processes, as well as demodulation, are the deliberate or inadvertent consequence of nonlinearity in a circuit or device.

9. In linear modulation, the amplitude of the modulation envelope is proportional to the amplitude of the modulating signal. This relationship does not hold in nonlinear modulation. Nonlinear modulation produces more than the pair of sideband frequencies generated by each modulating frequency in linear modulation. However, a suitable bandpass filter sometimes can cause the ultimate output of both linear and nonlinear modulation to be similar.

10. The bandwidth of resonant circuits in both transmitting and receiving equipment is a very important consideration. Ideally, it must present free passage to the sideband frequencies. Attenuation or phase shifting of the sidebands decreases the effective modulation factor and constitutes distortion of the modulating information.

Chapter 2

HIGH-LEVEL
AMPLITUDE MODULATION

Amplitude modulation may be applied to circuitry sections of a carrier amplifier or oscillator where carrier power levels are either low or high. Ordinarily, the plate circuit of a tube or the collector circuit of a transistor constitutes the high-level output of amplifiers and oscillators. The level of the carrier power associated with the grid or base input sections of these circuits is relatively low.

WHAT IS HIGH-LEVEL AMPLITUDE MODULATION?

When modulation is superimposed on the plate or collector d-c power supply, the process is appropriately termed *high-level modulation*. It follows that the application of modulation to the input circuit represents the process of *low-level modulation*. In low-level modulation the modulated carrier is boosted in power level as it emerges from the plate or collector. In high-level modulation, the applied modulating power must already be comparable in level to the carrier output. For these reasons, high-level modulation can only be effectively accomplished by modulators designed to deliver much greater power than is required in low-level modulation. Nonetheless, high-level modulation generally has the following advantages over low-level modulation:

1. The modulated-carrier amplifier achieves higher average efficiency.
2. Linear modulation up to 100 per cent is more readily accomplished.
3. Adjustment for optimum operation is less critical. In practice, both methods have their appropriate applications.

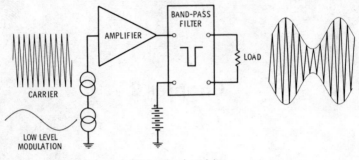

(A) Low-level modulation.

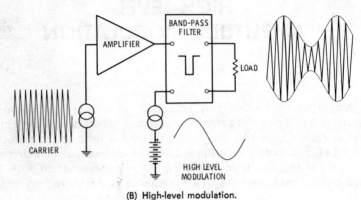

(B) High-level modulation.

Fig. 2-1. Amplitude modulation of an amplifier.

The block diagrams of Figs. 2-1 and 2-2 show the basic ideas involved. Additionally, it should be understood that high-level modulation of a driver stage in a transmitter constitutes low-level modulation of the transmitting system itself. This harmonizes with the reasoning with respect to a single stage, output stage, or oscillator alone. In such a transmitter, the stages following the modulated stage must provide proportional amplification because they amplify the actual modulation envelope. Appropriately, such amplifiers are known as *linear amplifiers*. Low-level modulation of the transmitter can also be imparted by modulating the grid or base circuit of the final amplifier. High-level modulation of the transmitter is brought about only through modulation of the d-c power supplied to the output circuit of the final amplifier.

The Nature of High-Level Amplitude Modulation

The modulating signal is applied to the output of the amplifier when high-level amplitude modulating an amplifier stage. The modulating interaction occurs at the output level where power is gen-

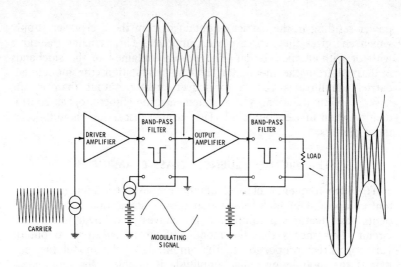

Fig. 2-2. An example of high-level modulation of the driver amplifier and low-level modulation of the output amplifier.

erally transferred to the antenna. However, the load may alternately be the input circuit of a still higher power-boosting amplifier. In such instances, the high-level modulation takes place in the previously mentioned driver stage, not in the driven stage(s). In principle, high-level modulation can be applied to any type of carrier-frequency amplifier. In practice, plate efficiency considerations most often dictate the use of tuned class-C amplifiers. Also in the interest of achieving the highest overall system efficiency, the modulator often makes use of a push-pull class-B arrangement. However, the basic concept of high-level modulation is not altered by the type ofi modulation equipment used. Low-power systems frequently utilize a single-ended class-A modulator as the source of the high-level modulating signal. Good optimization of efficiency and economy is often achieved through the use of a solid-state modulator and a modulated vacuum-tube class-C amplifier. It will be shown that the operating efficiency of all components involved in high-level amplitude modulation deserves very careful consideration. This includes the modulated amplifier, the modulator, and the associated d-c power supplies. The basic need for efficiency stems from the inherent redundancy and power-wasting nature of amplitude modulation itself. However, high-level amplitude modulation can be relatively efficient. When due attention is given to the characteristics of high-level amplitude modulation, this type of amplitude modulation often proves very useful.

Fundamental to high-level amplitude modulation is the source and distribution of power in the amplitude-modulated carrier. The power residing in the carrier is obtained from the d-c power supply which energizes the carrier power amplifier. This remains the same with or without modulation. The power contained in the sidebands is derived from the modulator. During modulation, the modulated-carrier amplifier is caused to deliver greater output than in the absence of modulation. These statements sometimes appear contradictory when first encountered. The ensuing discussion should clarify these matters.

THE HIGH-FREQUENCY CLASS-C AMPLIFIER

The high-frequency class-C amplifier constitutes such an important component of high-level modulation systems that a brief study of its basic features is important. It behaves as a linear modulating circuit. This means that the modulated-carrier envelope amplitude varies in direct proportion to the amplitude of the modulating signal. If the modulating-signal amplitude is doubled, the modulated-carrier envelope amplitude is doubled. If the modulating signal amplitude is halved, the modulated-carrier amplitude is halved. An insight of this characteristic is best gained by first investigating the operation of the class-C amplifier in the absence of modulation.

The circuits of typical class-C amplifiers are shown in Figs. 2-3 and 2-4. Two important features of such amplifiers are the tuned output circuit and the grid bias provision. Even before the operation of the overall amplifier is understood, a design and operational condition can be made with respect to the tuned output circuit. This resonant tank must support not only the carrier frequency itself but the sideband frequencies when modulation is applied. If this tank is too selective, the sidebands will not receive the same power amplification as the carrier. In such a case, a complex modula-

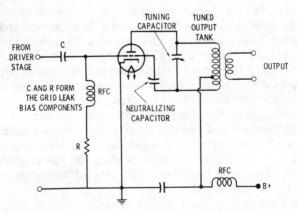

Fig. 2-3. Basic class-C amplifier with grid-leak bias.

ting signal will suffer distortion due to discriminatory attenuation of higher sideband frequencies. The average value of the modulation factor can also be reduced. In contradiction to this, we shall see that certain performance criteria of the class-C amplifier improve with increased selectivity of the output tank circuit. It follows that a compromise in the design of the output tank circuit is necessary.

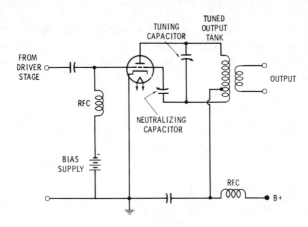

Fig. 2-4. Basic class-C amplifier with fixed bias.

The basic function of the grid bias in class-C amplifiers is to project operation sufficiently into the plate cutoff region so that plate current flows for less, often considerably less, than the 180 degrees corresponding to a half-cycle of carrier frequency. In many practical class-C amplifiers, plate current is restricted to the range of 120 to 150 degrees. The grid bias required to accomplish this is often in the vicinity of twice the cutoff value. Such operation completely destroys the ability of such amplifiers, either singly or paired, to provide proportional amplification such as must be obtained from amplifiers operating over the audio-frequency range. This is no drawback, since the area of concern is a single-frequency amplifier operating in the radio-frequency range.

Not only is the class-C amplifier unsuitable for proportional amplification, but its operation is more akin to that of a *switch*. This is brought about by restricting plate current to a small portion of the carrier cycle. Such an amplifier is deliberately driven into the region of plate-current saturation during its "on" interval. The operation is somewhat analagous to that of an electromechanical relay energized from an a-c source, as shown in Fig. 2-5. The relay may be made to produce a contact closure during only the positive portion of the input voltage applied to the relay coil. Since the diode is biased with a small voltage, the relay will not be pulled in until the input voltage overcomes this bias voltage. This effectively allows the relay contacts to close for something less than 180 degrees of the cycle, thus simulating class-C operation. (Significantly, the grid-cathode circuit of the amplifier tube does normally conduct current during a portion of the input.) This analogy is particularly applicable when it is also considered that the contacts of the relay can switch power levels greatly in excess of the input power applied to the relay coil. It is indeed more useful to think of the class-C amplifier as a power-boosting switch than as an amplifier in the usual sense. Such a viewpoint will gain validity as we proceed to investigate the function of the tuned output tank.

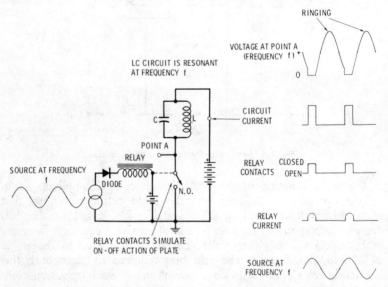

Fig. 2-5. Electromechanical analogy of a class-C amplifier.

When a tuned LC circuit is imparted pulses of current or voltage, the phenomenon of *ringing* occurs. Ringing is the conversion of the energy of such pulses into a sine wave of frequency corresponding to the self-resonance of the tuned circuit. As a general rule, ringing is enhanced by supplying narrow rectangular pulses at the same frequency as the self-resonance of the tuned circuit. Such production of ringing is known as shock-excitation. Improved shock-excitation comes about when the tuned circuit has a high Q, that is, a high ratio of energy storage in its reactive elements to energy dissipation due to its losses. Two things are meant by "improved" shock-excitation. First, there is less decay of ringing amplitude between the shocking pulses. Secondly, the harmonic energy contained in the pulses is more effectively attenuated. These two performance criteria are of course related.

The Resonant Output Tank

Although resonance can be achieved as the consequence of any number of inductance-capacitance combinations, the actual ratio of these two reactances is closely bound up with the realization of optimum performance. A high L/C ratio results in a high impedance at resonance, but tends towards lower Q than the converse ratio. Additionally, practical difficulties arise in coupling power out of such a circuit. This is particularly true when considerable impedance transformation is involved in the transference of power from the resonant tank to the load or feeder line. The low L/C ratio tank exhibits opposite behavior. It is particularly superior to the high L/C ratio tank in harmonic attenuation. Despite the relatively high Q of the low L/C tank, its higher losses tend to degrade the efficiency of the amplifier. The increased losses are due to the higher circulating currents present in such a resonant tank. Although losses in a resonant circuit always reduce its Q, it turns out that the low L/C ratio tank has both higher losses and higher Q than the high L/C ratio tank. (It may be recalled that a quartz crystal is an example of extremely high Q despite fairly high dissipative losses.) The Q is a function of both energy storage and losses in a resonant circuit.

Pentodes, tetrodes, and high-mu triode tubes operate at high plate voltages and low plate currents. Such tubes develop greater efficiencies when associated with high L/C ratio tank circuits. Medium- and lower-mu triodes favor lower L/C ratios, for the sake of achieving lower impedance.

Similar considerations apply to the pi network. The pi network is a low-pass filter, whereas the parallel tuned tank is a bandpass filter. The bandpass-filter characteristics serve no useful purpose between d-c and the lowest sideband frequency involved during modulation. The pi network provides frequency selectivity only where it is needed. This is the region above the highest sideband frequency involved during modulation. Here, its attenuation of harmonics is generally superior to that ordinarily attainable with the parallel tuned tank.

The circuit configuration of the class-C amplifier is inadvertently similar to circuits deliberately designed as oscillators. This becomes more apparent when one considers the connection to the tank circuit of the driving stage. The combination generally results in a good replica of a tuned-grid, tuned-plate oscillator. For this reason, the class-C amplifier will oscillate unless some precautionary measure is incorporated. With triode tubes, some neutralizing technique is necessary. This involves return of out-of-phase voltage to the grid so that insufficient positive feedback can exist to cause oscillation. The oscillatory condition, even when relatively subdued, tends to degrade the modulating characteristics of the class-C amplifier. It is very important that the design and construction of the class-C amplifier be such that virtually complete neutralization can be achieved and maintained throughout all modulating conditions. With tetrode and pentode tubes, neutralization can often be dispensed with. This results from the greatly reduced grid-plate capacitance of such tubes. However, the tendency toward self-oscillation always exists at the high frequencies employed in radiotelephony. Sometimes neutralization is found necessary even with such tubes.

Parasitic oscillations can occur at frequencies other than those in the immediate vicinity of the tank resonance. These are generally caused by resonances established between the inductances of connecting leads and stray capacitances. The physical layout of the amplifier has much to do with such undesired resonances. The primary rule to follow is to keep leads short, but at the same time endeavoring as much as possible to avoid proximity between input and output circuit components. A very low resistance (or a high-frequency choke) is sometimes inserted in the plate leads or grid leads to suppress the parasitic oscillation. Parasitic oscillations are not subject to neutralization by the operating-frequency neutralizing provision. Such parasitics often prove to be some of the most elusive preventatives of clean modulation.

D-C Grid Bias for the Class-C Amplifier

A simple method of securing the necessary negative grid bias for class-C operation is by means of a resistance inserted in the grid-return connection of the amplifier. This is known as grid-leak bias for the reason to be explained. As can be seen from Fig. 2-6, there is grid current for a portion of each carrier-frequency cycle. This occurs only while the carrier cycles are sufficiently positive to overcome the negative grid bias. But what is the source of the negative grid bias when no biasing battery or power supply is present? When the grid current occurs, the grid coupling capacitor becomes charged with a d-c potential so polarized as to apply negative bias to the grid as soon as grid current ceases. As a matter of fact, once this charging process has taken place, say as the consequence of one or several carrier cycles, no more grid current will flow until the charge dissipates itself. The capacitor acts as a battery with its negative terminal connected to the grid. However, if a resistance is connected between grid and cathode, some of this charge will leak off between successive carrier cycles. This being the case, a pulse of grid current occurs during the top positive excursion of each carrier cycle. Appropriately, the resistance connected to provide this function is called a *grid leak*. Bias so obtained is known as *grid-leak bias*.

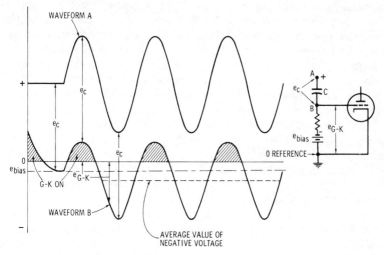

Fig. 2-6. Grid-leak bias.

An interesting and useful feature of grid-leak bias is its self-regulating property. The greater the carrier excitation, the more negative will be the average value of the d-c voltage developed across the grid coupling capacitor. Thus, fairly large variations in excitation will result in relatively small amplitude changes developed across the output tank circuit. A shortcoming of grid-leak bias is the fact that no negative grid bias is produced in the event carrier excitation is removed. Such an event can quickly destroy an expensive transmitting tube as a result of the great increase in plate current which would result. For this reason, grid-leak bias is often used in conjunction with fixed bias provided by a battery or a power supply. Protection against excitation failure may also be obtained from a cathode bias resistance. This, however, is objectionable because it subtracts from the d-c plate supply voltage.

A battery or power supply has the advantage of providing protection to the class-C amplifier tube in the event of carrier-excitation failure. It is best that such bias supplies have good regulation (low impedance). If the internal impedance of the bias supply is high, it may contribute to grid-leak bias. This is not necessarily a bad effect. As a matter of fact, the most satisfactory d-c bias supply for modulated class-C amplifiers is often a combination of power supply and grid-leak bias. However, in the interest of ease of adjustment, it is desirable to achieve this combination by a low-impedance d-c supply in conjunction with a physically discreet grid-leak resistance. The grid bias furnished by grid-leak action decreases in negative value in the vicinity of modulation crests. This is actually desirable as a means of compensating for the tendency for the modulation envelope to flatten out during the crest of the modulating cycle. Such flattening would destroy modulation linearity. This behavior of grid-leak bias is the equivalent of increasing the carrier excitation just when it is needed to provide a linear continuation of plate current increase. Deliberately degrading the regulation of the driving source serves a similar compensating function, but may introduce other problems in practical implementation.

Cathode-emitted electrons destined to contribute to grid current prior to the crest of the plate modulating cycle are drawn to the plate instead as modulation crest is approached. This is the reason that the bias developed by grid-leak action is influenced by plate-circuit events. The interaction is considerably less in certain tetrodes and pentodes.

The grid r-f choke is generally desirable. Often, when the grid leak is a sufficiently high resistance, it is found unnecessary to include the r-f choke. However, this should always be determined with the r-f choke in the grid circuit initially. Otherwise, it is not possible to know that the adjustment of optimum operation by varying the grid-leak resistance is not merely a compromise between d-c bias and carrier excitation. With the r-f choke in the circuit, the grid leak affects d-c grid only. After the amplifier has been adjusted for best operation, the need for this r-f choke can be quickly evaluated by observing whether grid excitation is reduced when the choke is shorted out. If there is no such effect, the choke can be dispensed with.

The path of d-c grid current must be completed through the bias source. Due to the direction of this current, the output voltage of an unregulated power supply tends to increase rather than fall as in the case of ordinary passive loads. As grid current increases, the actual loading on such supplies is relaxed. This often leads to difficulties in adjustment and in nonlinear modulation. Regulated power supplies employing shunt arms which behave as variable bleeder resistances are best. The regulated power-supply configuration which uses a variable series arm is likely to give trouble if used as a bias supply for a modulated class-C amplifier. Such a supply does not inherently provide a path for the d-c grid current. This shortcoming can sometimes be circumvented by means of a fixed bleeder resistance. The bleeder resistance, although connected across the output of such a supply, inadvertently functions as a grid-leak bias source, too. This may be acceptable, but the shunt-regulated supply in conjunction with a series-connected grid leak is better suited to the requirements of the modulated class-C amplifier. The shunt element may be a vr tube, a vacuum tube, a zener diode, or a transistor. In any event, such a shunt element must be capable of carrying whatever current is necessary for its operation, plus the grid current from the class-C amplifier.

Operating Considerations in the Class-C Amplifier

The widespread use of class-C amplifiers in both modulated and unmodulated service is primarily due to the high operating plate efficiency inherent with this mode of power amplification. The reason for this desirable situation is a unique functional relationship between the tube and the resonant output tank. One of the interpretations of the voltage-current relationship shown in Fig. 2-7 is that the internal tube dissipation due to the product of instantaneous plate current and plate voltage is low. This is because high plate

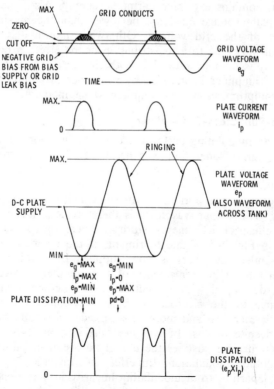

Fig. 2-7. Basic relations in the class-C amplifier.

voltage exists, for the most part, when the plate current is zero. Conversely, high plate current exists for the most part when the plate voltage is very low. This conclusion is aided by noting that the positive excursion of the voltage shock-excited in the resonant tank adds to the plate supply voltage but that the negative excursion subtracts from it. In order to enhance these fortunate events, the plate current pulse should be narrow in order to restrict its duration to the time corresponding to minimum plate voltage. In order to make the plate current pulse narrower, both negative grid-bias and grid drive must be increased. Eventually, grid losses impose a limit to this method of increasing operating efficiency. Moreover, excessively narrow pulses tend to decrease available output because less energy is provided to shock-excite the resonant output tank.

Causing the minimum value of plate voltage to be low is another way to increase operating efficiency. One of the ways in which this is brought about is through the use of a high impedance in the resonant output tank. This corresponds to a high L-to-C ratio. If, however, we go too far in this direction, bandwidth increases and the output contains excessive harmonic energy. Also, the minimum value of plate voltage must not be lower than the maximum positive value of the grid voltage. Otherwise, inordinately high grid current will flow due to a redistribution of the electron beam within the tube. It is obvious now that both the design and operation of the class-C amplifier is attended by a number of compromises. Additional compromises will be required when modulation is applied.

The Push-Pull Class-C Amplifier

Improved modulating performance as well as more efficient high-frequency carrier operation is generally forthcoming from class-C amplifiers incorporating a pair of tubes in a balanced or push-pull configuration. A representative circuit is shown in Fig. 2-8. Each tube conducts for a portion of alternate half-cycles of the carrier frequency. The output waveform is therefore less dependent on the flywheel effect of LC energy storage. Thus, the upper half-cycle depicted in Fig. 2-7 as due to ringing of the resonant output tank in single-ended amplifiers is now supplied by another tube. The tubes function as mirror images of one another. Twice as much power is developed with respect to the single-ended amplifier. A consequence of the electrical balance prevailing in the push-pull circuit is less critical and more broad-banded neutralization. This is attained despite the use of two neutralizing capacitors. The better neutralization alone justifies the use of push-pull amplifiers in high-level amplitude modulation. Imperfect neutralization is a common cause of departure from modulating linearity in single-ended amplifiers.

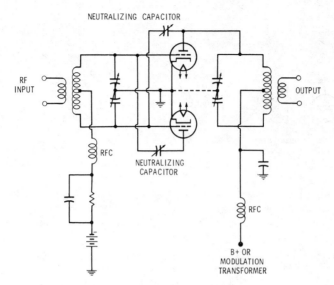

Fig. 2-8. Push-pull amplifier.

The push-pull arrangement provides more efficient operation at high carrier frequencies because tube capacities appear in series and are therefore effectively halved. Increased class-C amplifier efficiency relaxes the power requirement from the modulator.

In Fig. 2-8 the rotor of the split-stator output tuning capacitor may be left ungrounded if the amplifier is electrically balanced between its two halves. This lessens the probability of flashover during modulation peaks. The possibility of dispensing with the r-f choke and bypass capacitor is similarly dependent and is often realized. From the standpoint of modulation, a dividend is thus gained. In single-ended amplifiers this bypass capacitor must sometimes be compromised in value so that it will negligibly attenuate higher modulating frequencies, but still provide a low reactance to radio frequencies.

THE PLATE-MODULATION CHARACTERISTICS OF THE CLASS-C AMPLIFIER

If the d-c plate voltage of a class-C amplifier is changed, the carrier amplitude developed across the output resonant tank will change in direct proportion. This immediately suggests the possibility of amplitude modulation by varying the d-c plate voltage at the modulating rate. Indeed, this is the very principle of high-level amplitude modulation. Figs. 2-9 and 2-10 illustrate the relation underlying such modulation.

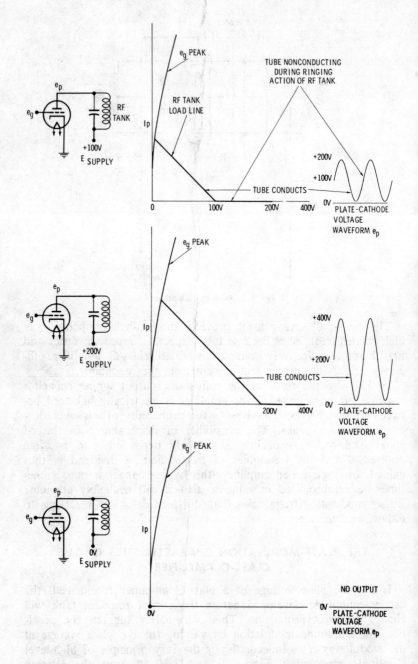

Fig. 2-9. Plate voltage waveforms of a class-C amplifier (for plate modulation use) for various supply voltages.

56

Fig. 2-9 illustrates the plate voltage waveforms and loadline analysis on the characteristic curve of a theoretical class-C amplifier for supply voltages of 0, 100, and 200 volts. When E $_{supply}$ is 0, there is no output. When E $_{supply}$ is 100 volts, the peak-to-peak value of e$_p$ is approximately 200 volts, and when E $_{supply}$ is 200 volts, the peak-to-peak value of e$_p$ increases to approxi-

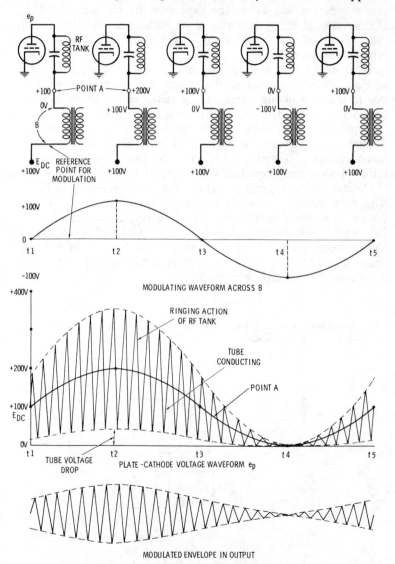

Fig. 2-10. Plate modulation.

mately 400 volts. Notice that the tube conducts in the lower portion of the waveform and that the upper portion of the waveform is due to the ringing action of the r-f tank.

Consider what occurs when the amplifier is operating with a supply voltage equal to 100 volts and the voltage is varied plus or minus 100 volts about this operating point. Then it can be seen that the output will indeed be dependent on the value of E_{supply}. If this value of E_{supply} is varied at an audio rate, the output amplitude of e_p will also vary at this audio rate. This occurs when a tube is plate-modulated.

Plate modulation is illustrated in Fig. 2-10. The effective value of E_{supply} occurs at point A, the bottom end of the r-f tank, and is due to the sum of the instantaneous values of the modulating voltages across point B, and E_{DC}. For example, at time T_2 the sum of the voltages is 200 volts and the peak-to-peak value of e_p is approximately 400 volts. At time T_4 the sum of E_{DC} and the modulating voltage is 0, and there is no r-f output. These conditions are during 100-percent modulation. A decrease in the magnitude of the modulating voltage across B will decrease the percent of modulation. The modulation envelope in the output occurs when the d-c component is removed in the transfer of energy, either capacitively or inductively, into the load. A little consideration will reveal the need for the modulator to supply an appreciable fraction of the power necessary to achieve a high modulation factor. Such power relations are a condition for high-level modulation.

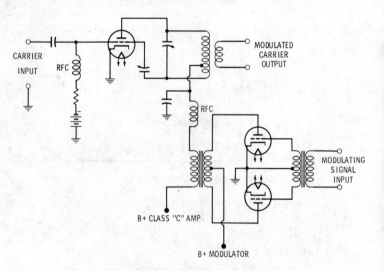

Fig. 2-11. Basic circuit arrangement of class-C amplifier that is high-level plate modulated.

The basic method of accomplishing high-level or plate modulation is shown in Fig. 2-11. The modulation transformer permits both modulator and modulated amplifier to operate at optimum loading. In other words, the modulation transformer provides an impedance-matching function. It will suffice here to state that push-pull, class-B operation, or a close approach to it, is the most efficient type of modulator. For our present purposes, we are more interested in the way in which modulation is brought about than the characteristics of the power amplifier which supplies the high-level modulating signal to the class-C amplifier. Due to its direct involvement in the overall efficiency of the transmitter or system, this type of modulator will receive relevant attention in Chapter 4, which deals with methods of minimizing wasted power in practical amplitude modulation.

Departure From Linearity in High-Level Modulation

Modulating linearity exists when the convolutions in the amplitude-modulation pattern faithfully reproduce the waveshape of the modulating signal. Under this condition, a distortionless demodulator in the receiving end of the communications system can recover the original modulating information. Such linear modulation is obtained when the amplitude of the modulated wave is directly proportional to the amplitude of the modulating signal. Ideally, this relationship should extend from 0- to 100-percent modulation. Such operation is not always readily forthcoming. In a class-C amplifier, the minimum instantaneous plate voltage should be, for best efficiency, approximately equal to the maximum instantaneous

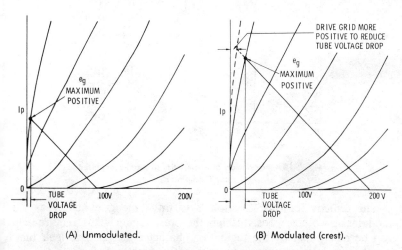

(A) Unmodulated.   (B) Modulated (crest).

Fig. 2-12. Load-line analysis of modulation nonlinearity.

grid voltage. This condition should prevail for all values of modulation factors from 0- to 100-percent for linear modulation. Unfortunately, this does not come about "naturally." Assuming 100 percent modulation, the minimum instantaneous plate voltage may be twice its nonmodulated value when the modulation voltage is at the crest of its cycle. This means that peak-to-peak carrier voltage developed across the tank circuit is less than it should be at this time. Consequently, we have flattening of the modulation envelope.

This may be illustrated graphically with the aid of the plate characteristics of the class-C amplifier and the load line, as shown in Fig. 2-12. If these are the plate characteristics of the theoretical tube used in Fig. 2-10, a load line equal to the impedance of the r-f tank can be drawn. This load line will be drawn as a straight line, neglecting any phase relations. In the condition shown in Fig. 2-12A, the amplifier is unmodulated, and when the r-f grid voltage e_g is maximum positive, the tube voltage drop is as shown. When the amplifier is modulated 100 percent, as in Fig. 2-12B, the plate voltage supply increases to 200 volts, as the modulating voltage reaches crest value. The tube voltage drop increases as shown at the time when the r-f grid voltage (e_g) is maximum positive. This effect can also be seen as a slight curve in the lower portion of the plate-cathode voltage waveform in Fig. 2-10. This departure from linearity is shown in Fig. 2-13.

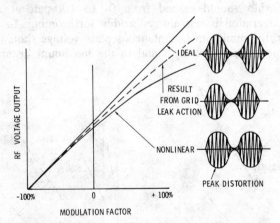

Fig. 2-13. Modulation characteristics of plate-modulated class-C amplifier.

The remedy for this situation is to drive the grid harder as the modulating voltage goes through the crest region. This requirement can be nicely met by the regulating characteristics of grid-leak bias. As the modulating cycle approaches the crest value, rectified grid current decreases as shown in Fig. 2-14. because electrons otherwise intercepted by the grid are drawn to the plate by the new higher plate voltage. This is accompanied by a reduction in grid-leak bias and therefore an increase in plate current. This, in turn, results in a lower value of instantaneous plate voltage just when it is needed for linearity. In practice, an optimum combination of fixed and grid-leak bias can generally be found which provides good modulating linearity for complete modulation of the carrier.

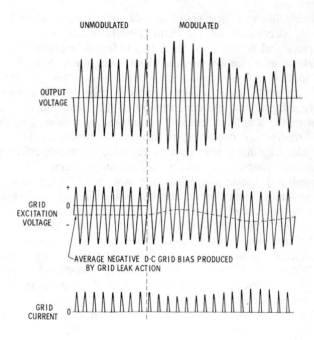

Fig. 2-14. Grid-leak bias action in the class-C amplifier that is plate modulated.

The inability of a tube to provide sufficient electron emission for plate current demand during modulating peaks can also be a deterrent to modulating linearity. Power supplies also often contribute to nonlinear modulation. The grid bias supply is particularly vulnerable to such malperformance. Such supplies must carry the current produced by grid rectification of the carrier excitation. These electrons flow into the grid bias supply. This often leads to disabling of the regulating circuitry of such supplies. Also, this type of "generator" load makes the worst of the inherently poor regulating characteristic of capacitor output supplies. Much better performance is generally obtained from bias supplies utilizing shunt regulators than from these with series-losser regulating elements.

The impedance match between modulator and class-C amplifier is important for the optimum performance of these individual units and for their successful operation mutually. Once the transmitter is designed, this match is greatly influenced by antenna loading. A mismatch of impedance between the modulator and the modulated amplifier is a common cause of both modulation nonlinearity and the inability to achieve complete modulation. A modulation transformer with tapped windings often proves to be well worth some additional expense.

Modulating linearity in class-C tetrode and pentode amplifiers is considerably dependent on optimum apportionment of modulation between plate and screen grid. Once this is found, acceptable modulating performance can be realized. The high power gain of these tubes simplifies grid excitation problems. It is often possible to dispense with neutralization. Success here is considerably influenced by operating frequency, the construction of the tube, and the physical layout of the amplifier stage. When low regeneration is attained, beneficial results are conferred to modulating linearity. In single-ended triode amplifiers, regeneration resulting from imperfect neutralization is a common cause of nonlinear modulation.

Grounded-grid triode amplifiers are not suitable for high-level modulation unless concessions are made for limited performance. A portion of the output power of such amplifiers is derived by direct addition of the excitation power. This part of the high-level carrier power does not receive modulation. Therefore, the modulating factor is restricted to something less than 100-percent. This can be 70 or 80 percent in triodes suitable for grounded-grid operation from other considerations. Attempts to extend modulation usually result in serious departures from linearity.

High-level modulation of transistors is practical, but is beset by unique difficulties witih respect to both modulation depth and linearity. These arise primarily from the variance of current gain, collector capacitance, and other transistor parameters throughout the modulation cycle. Special circuit techniques are often employed to compensate for these characteristics.

The Plate Modulation Transformer

The main function of the plate modulation transformer is to provide an impedance match between the modulator and the class-C amplifier. The impedance of the class-C amplifier is its d-c plate-to-cathode voltage divided by the d-c plate current drawn when delivering full unmodulated power into the antenna or load. The impedance of the modulator plate circuit is generally obtained from the manufacturer's tube data. For low-power systems, the modulator may be a single-ended class-A stage. For medium and high power, a push-pull class-B modulator is invariably used in order to attain optimum overall efficiency. The modulation transformer must have sufficient power-handling capacity to handle the average power output from the modulator. Additionally, the secondary winding must be of suitable wire size to avoid temperature rise from the d-c plate current to the modulated class-C amplifier. The transformer insulation must withstand a minimum of twice the class-C amplifier plate-supply voltage. A considerably higher voltage rating is generally necessary for the transformer insulation due to the effects of steep modulating waveforms and the possibilities of overmodulation. Modulation transformers often have tapped windings. This greatly facilitates attainment of optimum operation. An appreciable impedance mismatch may result in poor performance of the modulator itself. It will always result in more modulating power needed for complete carrier modulation than would be the case with matched impedance.

The winding associated with the modulator is the primary; the winding associated with the modulated class-C amplifier is the secondary. The impedance ratio is the impedance of the secondary with respect to that of the primary. The impedance ratio is equal to the square root of either the voltage or the turns ratio.

The average d-c current in the secondary of the modulation transformer is the same value as the plate current drawn by the class-C amplifier when unmodulated. This current serves no useful modulating function. It tends to subject the core of the modulation

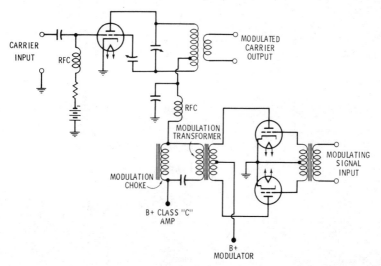

Fig. 2-15. Method of preventing d-c saturation effects in the modulation transformer using a choke.

transformer to saturation earlier than would otherwise be the case. Best design and operation of the modulation transformer is achieved by the expedient shown in Fig. 2-15. Here, the primary winding is spared d-c saturation by the flux-cancelling effect inherent in the push-pull configuration. The secondary winding is freed from core-saturation d-c current by the choke-capacitor arrangement, which still permits the needed a-c component of modulation to vary the instantaneous carrier-amplitude level.

Heising Modulation

Heising modulation is often cited as the simplest practical means of obtaining high-level amplitude modulation. This is somewhat debatable, for it depends on what manner of simplicity is obtained. It probably is true that Heising modulation is the oldest scheme in the evolution of the radio art. Also, it may qualify as the simplest method when relatively low power levels are involved. Fig. 2-16 shows a typical arrangement making use of the Heising technique. The salient feature of this circuit is the use of a modulation choke. This is in some ways equivalent to the use of a one-to-one transformer. Usually the Heising system incorporates a single class-A modulator tube. Such a modulator does not produce a voltage swing equal to the d-c power supply. Because of this, a resistor R is required to lower the d-c voltage to the class-C amplifier if 100 percent modulation capability is to be approached without excessive

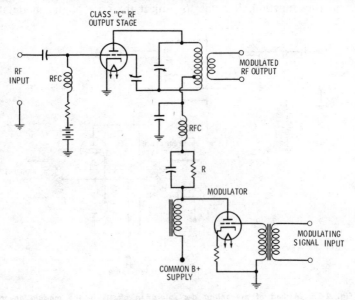

Fig. 2-16. Heising modulation.

distortion. The dropping resistor R must be bypassed at modulation frequencies.

In more modern versions of Heising modulation, a pentode class-A modulator tube has been employed. This has permitted omission of the dropping resistor and bypass capacitor with fair results for voice transmission. The resistor, of course, greatly reduces the efficiency of the system and is the prime reason this modulation technique has been largely replaced by transformer coupling. Heising modulation is often termed *constant-current modulation*. No unique operating principle is actually conferred by this terminology that does not also apply to the transformer coupling method if it too uses a class-A modulator.

Fig. 2-17 shows a Heising modulation scheme making use of a single beam-power tetrode modulator coupled to the Class-C amplifier through the autotransformer action of a tapped inductor. This is a very good arrangement for small transmitters. Full modulation capability is readily achieved without sacrifice of class-C amplifier

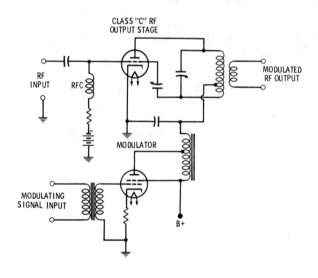

Fig. 2-17. Heising modulation with tapped inductor.

efficiency. At any given instant of time, the magnetic flux in the two core sections of the tapped inductor tend to cancel. This, in conjunction with the absence of an actual secondary winding, enables the use of a physically small inductor. Thus this scheme has been employed extensively in transceivers and portable transmitters.

High-Level Modulation of Tetrode and Pentode Amplifiers

Tetrode and pentode tubes often prove capable of superior performance to triodes when operated as class-C amplifiers. The possibility of dispensing with neutralization is in itself sufficient justification for the use of these tubes in many designs. The power amplification of these tubes is generally much greater than that of triodes. This makes it possible to use a lower-power driver. In some instances, this manifests itself in system layout by the elimination of an amplifier stage. The application of modulation to a tetrode or pentode amplifier requires some consideration beyond that applying to plate modulation of a triode. If only the plate circuit of a tetrode or pentode is modulated, the modulation will not be linear. When, during the modulation cycle, the screen voltage exceeds the plate voltage, the tube will be in its dynatron region. This region exhibits the undesirable parameters of nonlinearity and negative resistance. It is necessary to vary the screen grid voltage along with the plate voltage. In other words, the screen grid must be modulated also. Despite this, the basic modulation principle involved remains as high-level plate modulation.

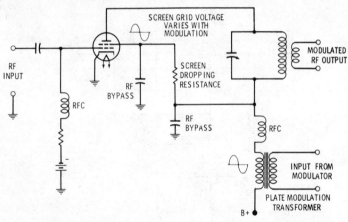

Fig. 2-18. High-level modulation of pentode or tetrode using series dropping resistance in the screen.

Fig. 2-18 shows the most common method of accomplishing linear modulation of a pentode or tetrode. Sometimes it is advantageous to bypass the screen dropping resistor in order to cancel the attenuating effect of the screen bypass capacitor at high modulating frequencies.

Fig. 2-19 shows a scheme utilizing a tertiary winding on the modulation transformer. This is an excellent approach in principle but it is not always readily applicable with available transformers

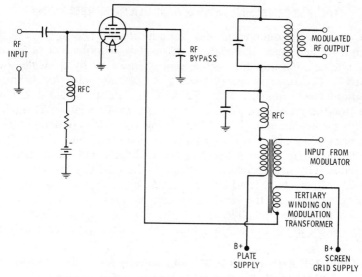

Fig. 2-19. High-level modulation of pentode or tetrode using transformer with screen-grid winding.

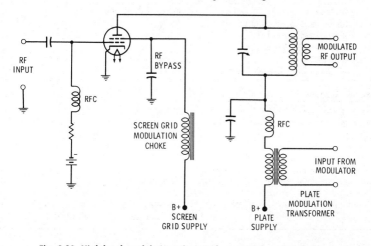

Fig. 2-20. High-level modulation of pentode or tetrode using choke.

Fig. 2-20 depicts a third approach. Here, modulation is applied to the plate only, but a choke having high impedance at modulating frequencies is inserted in the screen-grid circuit. This enables the screen grid to float at modulation frequencies. Under this condition, the screen grid tends to follow the plate modulation. No special consideration is involved with the suppressor grid in modulated pentodes.

100 PERCENT SINE-WAVE MODULATION RELATIONS

Conditions pertaining to design, adjustment, and operation of high-level amplitude modulation are usually described in terms of the relations existing for 100-percent modulation by a single sine wave. (The carrier is always assumed to be sinusoidal, too.) These relations are summarized in Table 2-1. The tabulated relations are, for the most part, valid for low- and intermediate-level modulation techniques also (exceptions being the last two items). The relations are particularly applicable to high-level modulation due to the matching required between the modulator and the modulated amplifier. Of considerable importance is the requisite for modulator power output. Note that this is stated to be one-half of the d-c power supplied to the modulated amplifier. The d-c input power to the modulated amplifier under the condition of no modulation is the same as its average d-c input power during full modulation.

Table 2-1. Relations in 100% Sinusoidally Modulated Output Wave With Respect to its Unmodulated Condition

Voltage and Current Relations	
Peak voltage of modulated wave	Twice that of unmodulated wave
Average voltage of modulated wave	Same as in unmodulated wave
Antenna or load current	1.225 times value for unmodulated wave
D-c plate current of modulated class-C amplifier	Same as for unmodulated wave
Voltage or current in each sideband	One-half carrier value
Power Relations	
Peak power of modulated wave	Four times unmodulated peak value
Average power in modulated wave	1.5 times unmodulated average value
Carrier power	Same as for unmodulated wave
Power in each sideband	One-quarter carrier power
Total power invested in sidebands	One-half carrier power
Fraction of total power in sidebands	One third
Fraction of total power in carrier	Two-thirds
Average d-c power to class-C amplifier	Same as with no modulation
Power demand from modulator	One-half of d-c input power supplied to modulated class-C amplifier

The important practical implication here is that an inefficient r-f amplifier makes the same demand on modulation power as an efficient one operating with equal input power. Of course, the efficient amplifier yields a modulated wave at a higher power level than does its low-efficiency counterpart. It is precisely here that the class-C amplifier asserts its superiority over, say, a class-A r-f amplifier. The same tube operating in class-A would deliver much lower r-f power, but this would not be accompanied by a relaxation in demand of modulation power.

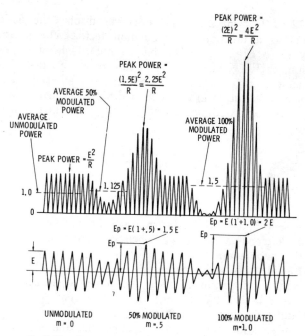

Fig.2-21. Output power relations versus modulation factor.

The relations of Fig. 2-21 are basic and provide initial insights even when different modulation waveforms and factors apply. The peak output power varies as the square of the peak output voltage of the modulation envelope. Inasmuch as peak output voltage doubles during 100 percent modulation, it follows that peak output power quadruples. Even though peak output power quadruples. average output power increases by only 50 percent. (This is the consequence of the fact that the power wave corresponding to a voltage sine wave is a sine-squared wave.) Consideration of the added sideband power leads more directly to the 50-percent power increase in the modulated wave. This being the case, antenna current during full modulation is $\sqrt{1.5}$ (or 1.225) times its unmodulated value. The d-c plate-current meter, on the other hand, cannot follow the equal amplitude excursions of the high-frequency current through it. It therefore indicates the same average current as with no modulation.

OPERATING PARAMETERS AS A FUNCTION OF MODULATION FACTOR

A more complete indication of power distribution and current involved in amplitude modulation is revealed by the curves of

Figs. 2-22, 2-23, and 2-24. These curves display the designated parameters as a function of modulation factor. The information given by these curves is applicable to both high- and low-level modulation. In Fig. 2-22 it is shown that relatively small increases in antenna current occur with moderate modulation factors. This curve is a plot of the ratio of modulated antenna current to modulation factor (expressed in percent). This is calculated from the equation:

$$I = I_o \sqrt{1 + \frac{m^2}{2}}$$

where,

I represents antenna or load current when modulated,

I_o is the antenna or load current when unmodulated,

m is the modulation factor.

By assigning a value of unity for I_o, a universally applicable curve results. For example, when the modulation factor is 100 percent, we see that the antenna or load current is 1.225 times the unmodulated value. This equation is derived from the amplitude-modulation equation taking into account that the summation of the carrier and two sideband terms involves three different frequencies. For this reason, the addition is not carried out in a simple arithmetical procedure.

Appreciable modulation can occur with little discernible change in the brilliancy of a lamp filament inserted in an antenna lead.

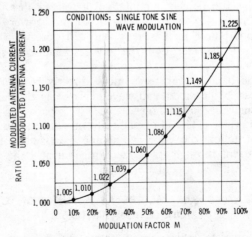

Fig. 2-22. Modulated/unmodulated antenna current versus modulation factor.

Although the glow of a lamp is often quite satisfactory as an indicator of unmodulated class-C amplifier operation, a high-frequency ammeter should be employed to enable accurate evaluation of modulating performance.

Fig. 2-22 shows the power in the modulated wave as a function of the modulation factor. This is a plot of the equation

$$P = P_o \left(1 + \frac{m^2}{2}\right)$$

where,

P represents power in the modulated wave as a function of modulation factor, m.

Here, P_o is the power when the carrier wave is unmodulated, that is, when the modulation factor is zero. By assigning a value of unity for P_o, a universally applicable curve results. For example, when the modulation factor is 100 percent, we see that the power contained in the modulated wave is 1.5 times the unmodulated value. This equation is derived from considerations similar to that of the current function but taking into account the fact that power is proportional to the squared value of current.

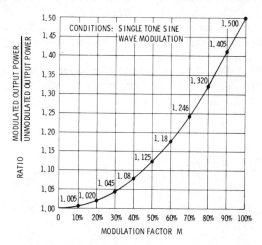

Fig. 2-23. Modulated/unmodulated output power versus modulation factor.

The information imparted by the curve of Fig. 2-23 is depicted in the two curves of Fig. 2-24 from a different viewpoint. These two curves show the distribution of power within the modulated wave as a function of modulation factor. Here, curve A indicates the total sideband power as a percentage of the carrier power. Thus, we see that at 100-percent modulation the total sideband power is one-half of the power of the carrier. Curve A is a plot of

the equation $P = P_o \dfrac{m^2}{2}$ where the symbols retain the meanings

described for Fig. 2-23. Here again, as a prelude to the material presented in the fourth chapter, it is only appropriate to observe that with a practical modulation factor such as 70 per cent about one-quarter of the power used in maintaining the carrier component is present in the sidebands for conveying modulating information. Actually, the situation is considerably worse than indicated in the curves thus far presented. Already mentioned has been the redundancy of information in the two sidebands. Applied here, this implies that only one-eighth of the power invested in the carrier component is truly involved in imparting information. In any practical transmitter, the modulated amplifier stage must necessarily operate below the ideal 100 percent plate efficiency. Any time we speak of, say a 100 watt, unmodulated carrier output level, the d-c input power to the amplifier producing this output is higher by the unavoidable losses. In order to obtain 100 watts of output at 70 percent plate efficiency, the d-c input power must be 100/0.70, or 141 watts. Such is the nature of the penalty exacted before modulation is applied. In high-level modulation, it is assumed that the operating efficiency of the modulated class-C amplifier remains constant during modulation.

Curve B of Fig. 2-24 depicts the sideband power as a fraction of the total power in the amplitude-modulated carrier wave. Curve B is a plot of the equation

$$P = \frac{P_o m^2}{2 + m^2}$$

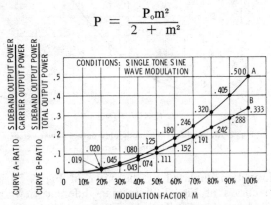

Fig. 2-24. Sideband power relations with carrier power and total power versus modulation factor.

where the symbols retain their previous meanings. We see that at 100 per cent modulation, the power contained in the two sidebands is one-third of the power making up the entirety of the amplitude-modulated carrier wave.

THE IMPORTANCE OF PLATE EFFICIENCY IN THE MODULATED CLASS-C AMPLIFIER

It is true that in high-level modulation the modulating signal is applied to the carrier output circuit of the amplifier stage. It should be clearly understood, however, that the resultant modulated carrier is the consquence of modulating the d-c power input to the modulated stage. This has a vital implication in terms of required modulating power. Suppose we have two class-C output amplifiers capable of the same unmodulated carrier output power. Assume one to operate at a relatively high plate efficiency and the other to be less efficient. The less efficient amplifier must, of course, consume more d-c power in order to deliver a given carrier power level to the load than is consumed by the more efficient amplifier. This may be tolerable in telegraphy, but when high-level modulation is applied, an additional penalty is exacted. The lower-efficiency amplifier will require more watts of modulating power to produce the same variation in *output* power level than would be required of the higher-plate-efficiency unit. For example, say we are interested in 100-percent modulation of 100 watts of carrier power.

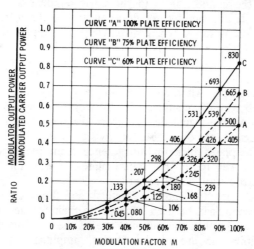

Fig. 2-25. Modulator power/unmodulated carrier power versus modulation factor for various plate efficiencies.

If the class-C amplifier were capable of 100 percent plate efficiency, the required modulating power would be 50 watts. An actual amplifier operating at a plate efficiency of 75 percent will require 66.5 watts of modulating power, whereas an amplifier operating at a plate efficiency of 60 percent will require 83 watts of modulating power to produce the same output conditions. This and the situation prevailing for other modulation factors are depicted in the curves of Fig. 2-25.

Another interpretation can be made as follows. A given modulating power and a given d-c power *input* to the class-C amplifier will result in the same modulation factor, regardless of the efficiency of the class-C amplifier. However, both the unmodulated and the modulated output-power levels will be less with a decrease in the efficiency. Inasmuch as two-thirds of the power contained in the amplitude-modulated wave at 100 percent modulation is wasted in the carrier, it becomes immediately apparent that one of the design and operational criteria for amplitude-modulation systems is efficient performance of the modulated amplifier.

THE TRAPEZOIDAL MODULATION PATTERN

A simple but extremely useful oscilloscopic technique for the evaluation of the modulation process involves the production of the trapezoidal pattern. This supplements the information generally attainable from the ordinary amplitude-modulation pattern. Fig. 2-26 shows the connections and the correspondences between the two patterns. It is generally not desirable to use the internal amplifiers of the oscilloscope when displaying the trapezoidal pattern. Link coupling, resonant tanks, and long, shielded coaxial cable can be advantageously employed to bring the sampled r-f signal from the output of the investigated amplifier to the vertical plates of the oscilloscope. Alternately, a simple pickup loop and a few feet of twisted wire often suffice. The horizontal plates are impressed with the modulating signal derived from the output of the modulator. Here, again, coaxial cable or twisted wire should be used. If the vertical plates pick up interference from the modulator, or if r-f finds its way to the horizontal plates, it will not be possible to obtain a clean trapezoidal pattern.

Whether or not the internal vertical and horizontal amplifiers of the oscilloscope can be used depends on their frequency response. Sometimes, this implies the optional use of the horizontal amplifier, but it prohibits the use of the vertical amplifier. In any event, as stated previously, dispensing with the internal amplifiers is worthy of consideration. Often, a resonant LC circuit is useful in providing more vertical deflection voltage.

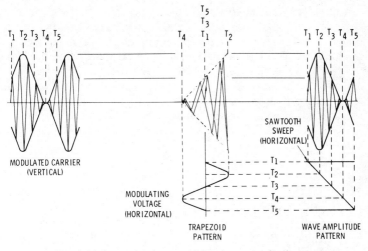

T_5
T_3
T_4 T_1 T_2

T_1 T_2 T_3 T_4 T_5

T_1 T_2 T_3 T_4 T_5

MODULATED CARRIER
(VERTICAL)

SAWTOOTH
SWEEP
(HORIZONTAL)

MODULATING
VOLTAGE
(HORIZONTAL)

TRAPEZOID
PATTERN

WAVE AMPLITUDE
PATTERN

(A) Graphical derivation of trapezoidal and wave-amplitude patterns.

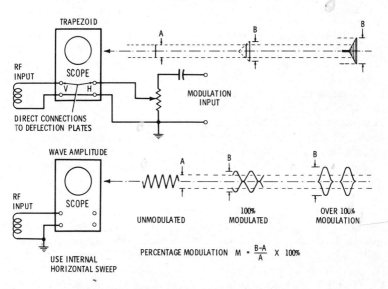

(B) Oscilloscope connections and sample patterns.

Fig. 2-26. Modulation monitoring with an oscilloscope.

The display of the trapezoidal pattern with a three-dimensional effect such as shown in Fig. 2-27 generally indicates fault with the measurement technique rather than with actual modulating performance. Here, the modulating sweep voltage (horizontal) is out of phase with the modulation envelope. This can readily happen if an attempt is made to derive the sweep voltage from a speech or driver amplifier rather than from the actual output of the modulator as it appears in the plate circuit of the modulated carrier amplifier. The RC network employed to sample the modulator output for the oscilloscope together with the capacitance of the connecting cable should be investigated when this type of pattern occurs with proper connections. Of course, the oscilloscope amplifiers, if used, become suspect when such a pattern is displayed.

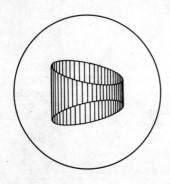

Fig. 2-27. Defective trapezoidal pattern
due to phase shift.

One of the features of the trapezoidal pattern is that its shape is not dependent on the shape of the modulating wave. Although a single-tone sine wave is generally used for initial evaluations, interpretations of modulating performance from this pattern are valid for any departure from the sinusoidal modulating signal. The straight slopes of the trapezoid are the consequence of a linear modulating relationship in the modulated amplifier regardless of the nature of the modulating signal. Several nonlinear trapezoidal patterns are shown in Fig. 2-28. The ratio of the long to the short vertical side is determined by the modulating factor. This, too, is true for any type of modulation. However, in order to have a sustained visual presentation of modulating performance, the modulating signal, whatever its waveform, should be periodic. After the operation is monitored with the repetitive modulating wave, the results with speech or other aperiodic waves may be observed as a final check on modulation.

As a consequence of the generation of the trapezoid as an independent function of the waveshape of the modulation, it follows that distortion in the speech amplifiers, or in the modulator itself, will not readily show up in the geometry of this pattern. Even though such distortion exists, the trapezoidal slopes will remain straight-sided as long as the class-C amplifier modulates linearly. In order to detect distortion of the modulating signal, it is necessary

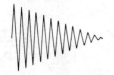

(A) Ideal linear 100% modulation.

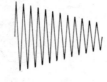

(B) Linear but incomplete modulation; possible cause —low modulator power.

(C) Nonlinear modulation; possible cause—improper grid bias and/or excitation.

(D) Nonlinear modulation; possible cause—regeneration from imperfect neutralization.

(E) Nonlinear and incomplete modulation; possible cause— parasitic oscillation and low modulator power.

(F) Nonlinear and incomplete modulation; possible cause—impedance mismatch between modulator and class-C amplifier.

Fig. 2-28. Trapezoidal modulation patterns of high level modulation.

either to monitor the modulator output directly or to display the amplitude-modulation pattern. When both the wave amplitude pattern and the trapezoidal modulation pattern are used, the prospect of attaining overall proper performance of the modulation system is greatly enhanced. The qualitative data provided by these two oscilloscopic techniques are almost indispensable for achieving optimum operation. It is otherwise difficult to secure the best combination of carrier drive, d-c bias, output loading, and impedance relations between modulator and amplifier.

A Percentage-Modulation Meter

Percentage of amplitude modulation of an r-f carrier can be determined with the use of the simple instrument schematically depicted in Fig. 2.29. The following requirements are necessary:

1. The strength of the signal picked up must be sufficient to operate diode D1 in its essentially linear region.
2. The modulating signal must be sinusoidal.
3. The frequency of the modulating signal must be high enough so as not to cause a response on the d-c carrier-level meter.
4. The modulation percentage meter must have a high impedance and be proportionately responsive to the rms level of the a-c modulation voltage impressed across it.

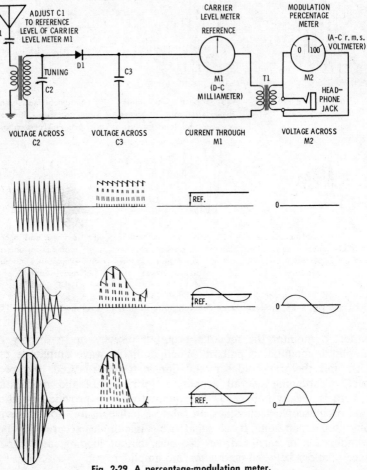

Fig. 2-29. A percentage-modulation meter.

Fortunately, all of these requirements are readily met. The carrier-level meter produces a deflection directly proportional to the peak-to-peak level of the unmodulated carrier. Modulation present does not alter this situation; the inertia of the meter movement precludes response to the modulating signal. From another viewpoint, the *average* value of the sinusoidal modulating signal is zero. This meter (M1) responds to the rectified carrier signal, and this d-c level is, as inferred, directly proportional to the peak-to-peak value of the carrier signal. This being the case, it should be apparent that if another meter is available to indicate peak-to-peak value of the modulating signal, sufficient information is presented to determine the percentage of amplitude modulation. Moreover, if the carrier-level meter is set to a predetermined reference deflection, the second meter can be calibrated to read modulation percentage directly.

To accomplish this, transformer T1 and meter M2 are inserted in the circuit. The transformer, unlike meter M1, responds to the modulating signal separated from the carrier by diode D1. The separation is made virtually complete by the capacitor C3, which bypasses the residual carrier component. Thus, the voltage developed in the secondary of T1 is directly proportional to the original modulating signal. This voltage is indicated by the modulation percentage meter. This meter has a high impedance in order to prevent loading effects. Although meter M2 deflects in response to the rms value of the voltage impressed across its terminals, the peak-to-peak value of a sine wave differs from its rms value by a constant factor (p-p value is 2.8 times the rms value). Thus, it can be said that the two meters provide indications directly proportional to the peak-to-peak values of the unmodulated carrier, and of the modulating signal. This enables calibration of the scale of meter M2 in terms of modulation percentage. Such calibration will be valid when meter M1 indicates its predetermined carrier reference level. With no modulation, meter M2 will read zero. With modulation, meter M1 will not change its indication, but meter M2 will then indicate the percentage of modulation.

Variable capacitor C1 is used for adjusting the reference deflection of meter M1. However, it is generally necessary to have additional control; this is achieved in practice by changing the physical location of the instrument and/or by varying the amount of antenna exposed to the signal. The latter control is conveniently accomplished through the use of a telescoping whip antenna. In all cases, however, tuning capacitor C2 should be first adjusted to produce the *greatest* possible deflection of meter M1.

A change in the deflection of meter M1 when modulation is applied to the tranmitter indicates carrier-level shift. A decrease in deflection of meter M1 generally is the consequence of non-linearity in the modulated class-C amplifier. An increase in deflection of M1 generally results from overmodulation.

All that has been said with regard to the use of the modulation percentage meter involves a single-tone sinusoidal modulating signal. For other modulating waveshapes, meter M2 would have to be a peak-indicating type, actually responsive to peak voltage, regardless of waveshape.

THE PREVENTION OF FREQUENCY MODULATION AND CARRIER SHIFT

The bandwidth required to accommodate the sideband products of modulation suffice to make interference-free communications difficult. This is particularly true in the light of the great number of stations broadcasting within the relatively narrow confines of available band space for radiotelephony. If, during amplitude modulation, simultaneous frequency modulation also occurs, additional band space is unnecessarily consumed. Then the interstation interference problem is agitated. Oscillators are prone to frequency shift when their load changes. Simple self-excited oscillators are particularly vulnerable. Modulation of the plate circuit of an amplifier affects the load characteristics of its grid circuit. This effect occurs at the modulation frequency. Thus, a simple self-excited oscillator driving a high-level modulated amplifier would be subjected to frequency modulation. Well-designed electron-coupled oscillators and vfo's display greater immunity to the effects of load variation. Crystal oscillators are the best in this respect.

Although the inherent stability of the oscillator is always an important consideration in the prevention or minimizing of frequency modulation, the design layout information indicated in Fig. 2-30 applies in a relative way. The salient feature of the arrangement depicted in Fig. 2-30A is the presence of two buffer stages, one of which is a frequency multiplier. Frequency multipliers provide

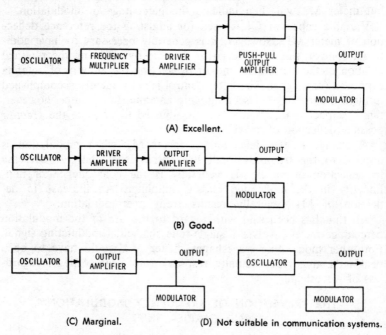

(A) Excellent.

(B) Good.

(C) Marginal.

(D) Not suitable in communication systems.

Fig. 2-30. High-level modulation systems illustrated in terms of minimizing frequency modulation.

particularly good isolation. The simpler sequence shown in Fig. 2-30B is capable of good performance, but more emphasis must be paid to design and operating techniques. The arrangement in Fig. 2-30C is even simpler, but is definitely subject to frequency modulation. Much depends on the oscillator, power-supply regulation, neutralization, loading required from the oscillator, and adjustments. The high-level modulated oscillator of Fig. 2-30D is not considered suitable for communications use. However, this scheme is often encountered in test and measurement equipment. In such use, the modulation factor is generally restricted to a maximum of 30 percent.

In all design layouts, it is very important to isolate the oscillator power supply from any d-c voltage carrying modulation. The best form of isolation consists of the use of a separate regulated supply. All oscillators tend to deviate frequency as a consequence of varying plate voltage. Even such a relatively complex arrangement as shown in Fig. 2-30A could produce severe frequency modulation if the oscillator plate supply varies with modulation.

The High-Level Modulated Oscillator

Despite its susceptibility to frequency modulation the high-level modulated oscillator is encountered in various services. As mentioned, test and measurement equipment often use modulated oscillators. In the past, this technique enjoyed widespread popularity in maritime radio-communications. Very low power communications still make use of the economy and simplicity provided by the modulated oscillator. For example, this modulation method is often found in phonograph oscillators and in carrier intercommunications. A

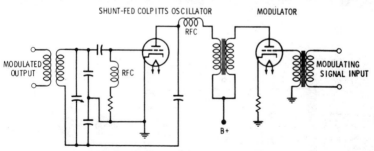

Fig. 2-31. High-level modulated oscillator.

representative modulated oscillator is shown in Fig. 2-31. Here, a shunt-fed Colpitts oscillator is plate modulated in a manner similar to that previously described for class-C amplifiers. Other oscillator configurations such as the Hartley, the tuned-plate, tuned-grid, etc. lend themselves equally well to such modulation. The electron-coupled oscillator of Fig. 2-32 modulates with considerably less frequency deviation than the simpler, self-excited oscillators. This is because such an arrangement is roughly the equivalent of an oscillator-amplifier system. The screen grid acts as the plate of a triode oscillator. The actual plate of the tube then functions some-

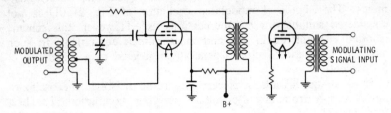

Fig. 2-32. Electron-coupled modulated oscillator.

what as the output electrode of a subsequent amplifier stage. There is considerable isolation between the plate circuit and the oscillator circuit proper. However, due to the dynatron characteristics of tetrode tubes, the plate modulation must be kept quite low in order to exploit such carrier-frequency isolation.

An interesting method of *preventing* amplitude modulation is shown in Fig. 2-33. This was at one time very widely used in medical diathermy and may still be encountered in industrial high-frequency heating work. Here a push-pull, self-excited oscillator also rectifies the raw a-c signal applied to it. Actual high-frequency, push-pull operation is not attained. Rather, one tube at a time assumes the burden of oscillation as its plate becomes positive with respect to its cathode. If the power line frequency is 60 cps, the

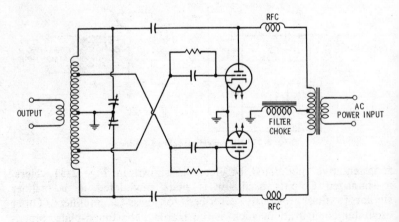

Fig. 2-33. Self-rectifying oscillator.

two tubes oscillate for alternate periods of approximately 1/120 of a second. During such oscillatory periods, the filter choke tends to hold the plate current constant. This arrangement produces considerably less amplitude modulation and attendant frequency modulation than would occur from the more conventional approach of energizing both oscillator tubes or a single oscillator tube directly from alternating current.

HIGH-LEVEL MODULATION OF TRANSISTORS

The basic approach to high-level modulation of transistors is similar to that of tubes. Here, too, the modulating source is inserted in series with the power supply. As with modulated tube amplifiers, the objective is to at least have the possibility of 100-percent modulation with good linearity. It has been pointed out that such performance is not generally forthcoming with tubes, due to the requirement of increased grid excitation for high modulating factors. Fortunately, the variation of grid current in conjunction with the regulating characteristics of grid-leak bias can provide the compensation necessary to restore linearity to the modulating behavior of the tube. Such compensation is not found to work well with transistors. The tendency towards compression of the modulation envelope is much more severe in the modulated transistor than in the modulated tube. Due to the forward-conduction requirement of the base-emitter diode the operation of the amplifier tends to approach class B, particularly with the added excitation needed for high modulating factors. In contrast, the tube is producing output power before its control electrode (grid) is drawing current. This enables the grid-leak developed bias to exert a greater control of the output. Two other factors exist which tend to flatten the modulation envelope long before 100 percent modulation can be reached. It is commonplace for transistors to suffer a decrease in current gain in the face of such heavy increase in power output as demanded by 100 percent modulation. Because of this, considerable increase in excitation power is required to prevent compression of the modulation envelope at the crest point of the modulation.

A second reason why the modulating factor tends to be limited involves feedthrough. This is a phenomenon which greatly exceeds any analogous action in vacuum tubes. When the modulation is at its trough, the collector-emitter voltage should be zero. Unfortunately the collector-base diode behaves as a voltage-controlled capacitor (varactor). As such, its capacitance will be greatest when its terminal voltage is least. This condition occurs approximately when, at the trough of the modulating cycle, the collector-emitter voltage is driven towards zero. As a consequence, considerable carrier power feeds through. This condition worsens if the base-collector junction becomes forward biased. This prevents the attainment of full modulating capacity in the downward direction. Thus, modulation encounters limits in both the upward and the downward regions of the modulation envelope.

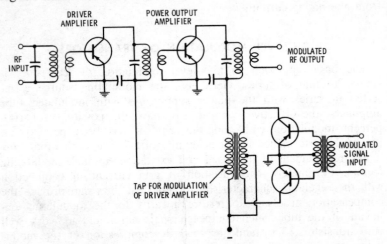

Fig. 2-34. Simultaneous modulation of power output stage and driver stage in transistor transmitter system.

In order to circumvent these modulating limitations, measures must be taken to force the instantaneous collector voltage to reach twice the unmodulated value in the upward direction and zero voltage in the downward direction. The best way to accomplish this while preserving reasonable modulating linearity is to simultaneously modulate the driver stage. One way of doing this is illustrated in Fig. 2-34. Here, a fraction of the available modulating voltage is impressed on the driver stage. The output stage then functions for the most part as a high-level modulated amplifier, but partially as a linear amplifier as well. A linear amplifier provides proportional amplification to a modulated carrier and, from a system basis, constitutes low-level modulation. By this expedient, it is possible to achieve fairly linear modulation up to 100 percent. This is always a worthwhile performance characteristic, even though the average modulating factor in actual operation is well below complete modulation. A modulated amplifier, either tube or transistor, which accepts modulation only up to, say, 70 percent before departure from linearity would be restricted to an average modulating factor of perhaps 45 percent in order to safeguard against distortion and splatter on occasional modulation peaks.

Another useful expedient with transistor r-f amplifiers involves the tapping of the collector connection down from the "hot" end of the tank inductor. This improves the operating Q of the tank. If carried far enough, it is often found that neutralization can be dispensed with, providing that some unbypassed resistance is present in the emitter lead. Otherwise, the same approach to neutralization can be carried out as with tubes. Although a good measure of empirical evaluation is generally indicated for such transistor systems, once optimum relationships are determined, excellent modulating performance can be attained.

Method of Increasing Modulation Depths in Transistor Transmitter

Another approach for overcoming shallow modulation in the transistor output stage is shown in Fig. 2-35. This technique pro-

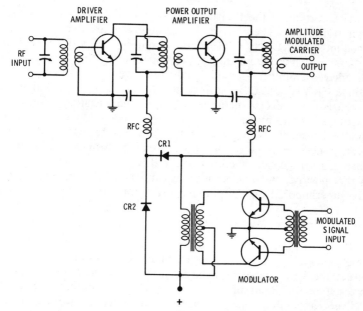

Fig. 2-35. Method of increasing modulation depth in transistor transmitter.

vides greater depth of modulation but with a considerable departure from modulating linearity. This nonlinearity is acceptable insofar as concerns intelligibility of speech. Moreover, it is free from splatter effects. The distortion of the modulating information is benign and is considered a good trade-off for increased "talk power." The modulation envelope developed is shown in Fig. 2-36. Inasmuch as the carrier is not cut off during downward modulation, no splatter is produced even when upward modulation exceeds the peak level corresponding to 100 percent modulation. The extra sidebands created by this unsymmetrical modulation do not extend sufficiently into the spectrum to produce interferences.

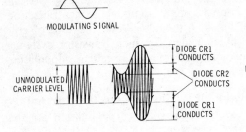

Fig. 2-36. Modulation envelope produced by partial modulation of driver amplifier in Fig. 2-35.

The portion of the transmitter shown in Fig. 2-35 makes use of npn transistors. These have d-c polarization analogous to that of vacuum tubes. Diode CR1 conducts during the positive (upward) excursion of the modulating cycle. Thus, during this period of time, the driver amplifier is modulated along with the power amplifier. Diode CR2 is not active during this portion of the modulating cycle because it is reverse polarized. During the negative (downward) excursion of the modulating cycle, the conducting states of the two diodes alternate. Now, diode CR1 becomes reverse-biased. However, diode CR2 now conducts. CR2 thereby provides the necessary current to the collector circuit of the driver amplifier. The net effect is that positive, but not negative, excursions of the modulating cycle are superimposed on the nominal driver-amplifier supply voltage.

Pulse-Amplitude Modulation

If the amplitude of a waveform is periodically sampled for very brief intervals, the data thus accumulated are sufficient to reconstruct the wave with excellent fidelity. The narrow pulses are impressed at the input of a low-pass filter. The output of the filter delivers a continuous wave bearing the trace of the original. In so doing, we have not made use of the relatively long time intervals between the succession of sampling pulses. The obvious thing to do here is to use these intervening spaces for pulses conveying amplitude information about other waveforms. Such time multiplexing of signals is employed in telemetry in order to conserve spectrum space. Several information channels are thereby time-shared and propagated over substantially the same bandwidth which would otherwise be required for a single channel. Fig. 2-37 illustrates the basics of such a system. Note that the commutators are synchronized. In this way, a particular low-pass filter receives only those pulses corresponding to a single information channel. This is necessary because otherwise a given low-pass filter would integrate pulse-amplitude information relating to more than one original waveform, and a confused output would be obtained. Although mechanical commutation has proved feasible for such techniques, reliable operation is considerably dependent on associated electronic synchronizing circuitry. For the actuation of such circuits, synchonizing pulses are simultaneously transmitted with the actual amplitude information.

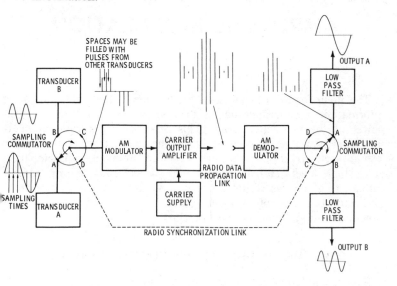

Fig. 2-37. Use of pulse-amplitude modulation for multiplexing data in telemetry.

It would be only natural to seek the number of samples needed of the scanned waveform in order to be able to subsequently restore its shape. Surely, it would appear to be a case of the more, the better. Surprisingly, however, it is a mathematical fact that the sampling rate need be only twice the highest frequency involved in the waveform. Thus, if a sine wave of frequency x cycles per second is to be sampled, it is only necessary to use a sampling rate of $2x$ cycles per second. If the sampled wave is nonsinusoidal, it should be ascertained which is the highest harmonic having appreciable bearing on the shape. Then, sampling must be carried out at twice the rate of the frequency pertaining to this harmonic. In all cases, the lowpass filter should enter its cutoff region at a frequency less than one-half of the sampling rate.

Chapter 3

LOW- AND INTERMEDIATE-LEVEL AMPLITUDE MODULATION

The main feature of high-level modulation is that the modulating information is superimposed on the d-c plate (or collector) input power of the modulated stage. This process occurs with modulating-signal power levels comparable to the power level of the carrier output itself. It is thus that we say such modulation is imparted at a "high level." What, then, is "low-level" modulation? Almost without thinking, we would ascribe modulations which do not comply with this description as low level. Several examples of such "low-level" modulation can now be cited.

LOW- AND HIGH-LEVEL MODULATION COMPARED

Suppose a buffer or driver amplifier in a succession of class-C amplifiers is high-level modulated. That is, its plate circuit receives power from both a d-c supply and an a-c modulator. The modulated output from this stage is subsequently boosted in power level by one or more "linear" amplifiers before delivery to the antenna. Such a *transmitter* is said to be low-level modulated despite the high-level modulation of the intermediate stage. From the systems viewpoint, a similar type of low-level modulation is brought about when modulating signal and carrier excitation are simultaneously applied to the control grid of the final carrier amplifier. The required power level from the modulator to accomplish such modulation is very much less than that needed for plate modulation even though the final amplifier is being directly modulated. We say such modulation is imparted at a "low level." The same reasoning applies when modulation of the final carrier amplifier is accomplished by injection of the modulating signal in the screen-grid or suppressor-grid circuits of multielement tubes. Modulation produced by diodes and by absorption techniques also belong to the low-level family.

Application of modulating power to the cathode circuit of a class-C amplifier combines features of both plate (high-level) and grid (low-level) modulation. Therefore, cathode modulation is conveniently classified as intermediate-level modulation. Intermediate-level modulation also occurs in some transistor transmitters. Because of carrier leak-through and variation of transistor parameters over the modulating cycle, it is difficult to approach complete modulation of the final transistor stage by applying modulating power to its collector circuit alone. Modulation is often simultaneously applied to the driver stage. From a systems viewpoint, such a transmitter is both high-level and low-level modulated. It is thus that we say such a transmitter is intermediate-level modulated.

When we investigate these matters a little more in detail, we find that relative power level is not the only criterion for distinguishing high-level modulation from low-level modulation. In high-level modulation, the plate efficiency of the modulated amplifier remains high and substantially constant throughout the modulating cycle. Practical plate-modulated class-C amplifiers commonly operate at plate efficiencies in the 70 percent to 80 percent range. For complete modulation of the carrier, both effective plate current and effective plate voltage double at the crest of the modulating cycle. The peak instantaneous power is therefore four times the power prevailing with no modulation. We are now prompted to inquire whether this relationship holds true for low-level modulation.

From the basic principles of amplitude modulating a carrier, we would feel safe in assuming that an antenna or other lead must "see" identical relationships whether amplitude modulation has been accomplished via high or low modulation. Here is a paradox. The d-c voltage applied to the plate circuit of the low-level modulated amplifier is not varied by the modulating information. The plate current is, as in high-level modulation, doubled for 100 percent modulation, although from a different causative factor. This might lead us to suspect that 100 percent modulation could not be achieved because the attendant quadrupling of carrier power requires doubling of both plate current and plate voltage. Actually, despite the constancy of applied d-c voltage, the voltage developed across the output resonant tank does double at the crest of 100 percent modulation. The low-level modulated amplifier does produce the same type of amplitude-modulated wave as is obtained in high-level modulation. What, then, explains the amplitude dependency of output carrier voltage as well as output carrier current on modulation?

An interpretation of the two types of modulation is shown in Fig. 3-1. Here, the theoretical tube is used again along with the load line, both being the same for the two types of modulation. The

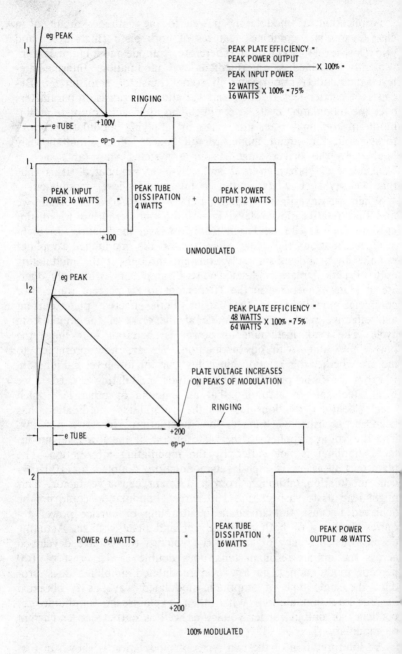

PEAK PLATE EFFICIENCY =

$$\frac{\text{PEAK POWER OUTPUT}}{\text{PEAK INPUT POWER}} \times 100\% =$$

$$\frac{12 \text{ WATTS}}{16 \text{ WATTS}} \times 100\% = 75\%$$

RINGING

eg PEAK

I_1

+100V

e TUBE

ep-p

I_1

| PEAK INPUT POWER 16 WATTS | = | PEAK TUBE DISSIPATION 4 WATTS | + | PEAK POWER OUTPUT 12 WATTS |

+100

UNMODULATED

PEAK PLATE EFFICIENCY =

$$\frac{48 \text{ WATTS}}{64 \text{ WATTS}} \times 100\% = 75\%$$

eg PEAK

I_2

PLATE VOLTAGE INCREASES ON PEAKS OF MODULATION

RINGING

e TUBE

+200

ep-p

I_2

| POWER 64 WATTS | = | PEAK TUBE DISSIPATION 16 WATTS | + | PEAK POWER OUTPUT 48 WATTS |

+200

100% MODULATED

(A) Plate modulation.

Fig. 3-1. Comparison of plate and control-grid

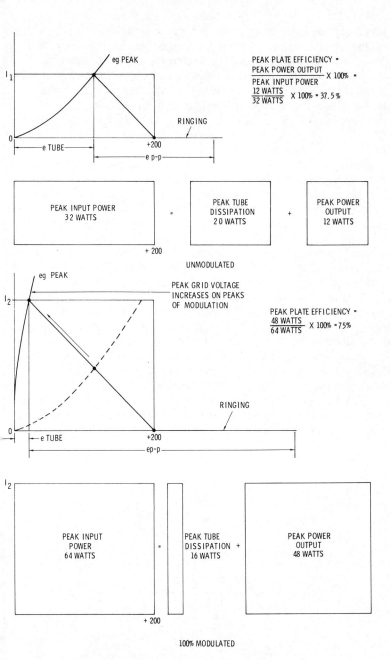

PEAK PLATE EFFICIENCY =
$$\frac{\text{PEAK POWER OUTPUT}}{\text{PEAK INPUT POWER}} \times 100\% = \frac{12 \text{ WATTS}}{32 \text{ WATTS}} \times 100\% = 37.5\%$$

PEAK INPUT POWER 32 WATTS = PEAK TUBE DISSIPATION 20 WATTS + PEAK POWER OUTPUT 12 WATTS

UNMODULATED

PEAK GRID VOLTAGE INCREASES ON PEAKS OF MODULATION

PEAK PLATE EFFICIENCY =
$$\frac{48 \text{ WATTS}}{64 \text{ WATTS}} \times 100\% = 75\%$$

PEAK INPUT POWER 64 WATTS = PEAK TUBE DISSIPATION 16 WATTS + PEAK POWER OUTPUT 48 WATTS

100% MODULATED

(B) Control-grid modulation.

modulation having the same output power.

power output is the same in both cases, but the plate supply voltage in the plate-modulation configuration is one-half of what it is in the control-grid modulation configuration. In both cases the area within the various E and I boundaries represents power. In Fig. 3-1A, plate modulation, the tube is dissipating less than the input power since the grid is driven positive enough so that the peak plate voltage when conducting is low. The efficiency is quite high in both modulated and unmodulated conditions. The majority of the power is delivered to the load.

In Fig. 3-1B, control-grid modulation, the grid is not driven as positive in the unmodulated condition, so to get the same power out, the plate voltage must be increased. This, however, increases the total input power and the tube dissipation. In fact, the output power is less than the tube dissipation, a very wasteful condition. Plate efficiency is low. When the 100 percent modulated (crest) condition is reached, the tube dissipation drops, power input increases, and power output quadruples, equaling the 100 percent modulated plate-modulation conditions at this time. It can be seen that the input power in the control-grid modulation condition is twice as much as the input power in the plate modulation condition, unmodulated, but equal when 100 percent modulated (crest). Also, the tube dissipation in the control-grid modulation condition is five times as much as in the plate modulation condition when unmodulated, but equal when 100 percent modulated (crest).

In the technical literature, low-level modulation is referred to as variable-efficiency modulation. Conversely, high-level modulation is often referred to as constant-efficiency modulation. In both modulations, changes in plate current and in plate voltage are produced

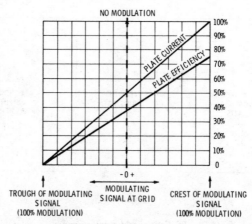

Fig. 3-2. Plate efficiency and plate current versus modulating signal at grid for control-grid modulation.

as a linear function of the modulating signal. The means of attaining these ends are different, however. We shall see that low-level modulating techniques merit study apart from high-level modulation.

Let us extend scrutiny to the significance of variation of plate efficiency in the low-level modulated amplifier. For 100 percent modulation, the plate efficiency will vary from zero to the operating efficiency of a class-C amplifier, say 75 percent (See Fig. 3-2). Specifically, the plate efficiency will be 75 percent at the crest of the modulating cycle. At the trough of the modulating cycle, the plate efficiency will be zero. Half way between the trough and the crest of the modulating cycle the plate efficiency will also be at its half-way point, or 37½ percent. Of course, this half-way point corresponds to the unmodulated carrier condition. (When the modulating sine wave crosses its zero axis, no modulation is applied.) This being the case, we have an amplifier which commences business with a plate efficiency of 37 percent prior to modulation. The same amplifier tube would be operating at a plate efficiency of 75 percent if it were high-level modulated. As a first approximation, a given r-f power tube will deliver about one-fourth as much carrier power for low-level modulation as may be attained from high-level modulation when operated at the same d-c plate voltage. At the crest of 100 percent modulation, the low-level modulated amplifier quadruples its power output, thereby just equaling the no-modulation output it would deliver if it were high-level modulated. See Fig. 3-3.

High-level modulation involves the adding of power to a high-efficiency carrier amplifier. Low-level modulation is more in the nature of operating the carrier amplifier as a variable losser. As such, deliberate sacrifice of efficiency is brought about in order to establish a midway-operating point. Modulation then enhances and diminishes this plate efficiency throughout its cycle. Obviously, the average efficiency must be less than that for high-level modulation. Although it is low, we shall see that it is quite fortunately higher than the 37½ percent corresponding to no modulation. That is, the sustained presence of modulation provides an increase in average carrier output and in average plate efficiency over the no-modulation values. Yet, because of the disparity of attainable carrier outputs in the two modulating methods, we are inclined to ask, "Why use low-level modulation?"

Why Use Low-Level Modulation?

One of the strongest arguments for the use of low-level amplitude modulation is the economy resulting from the relatively small power required from the modulator. Hundreds of watts can be completely modulated by means of receiving-type tubes employed in modulators with outputs not exceeding several watts, or at most,

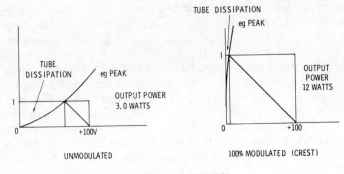

UNMODULATED

100% MODULATED (CREST)

CONTROL-GRID MODULATION

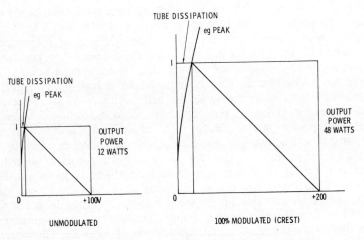

UNMODULATED

100% MODULATED (CREST)

PLATE MODULATION.

Fig. 3-3. Comparison of plate and control-grid modulation using equal d-c plate supplies.

several tens of watts. This argument is supported by the assertion that net economy prevails notwithstanding the fact that a much larger output tube(s) is required in the final carrier stage to produce the same carrier output that would be obtained from a smaller tube with high-level modulation. Actually, the size and the complexity of the transmitting installation, as well as many other factors, enter into a choice between high- and low-level modulation. Not all of the considerations are economic. The issue is complicated by the relative importance paid to modulation linearity, ease of adjustment, isolation from the oscillator, and tube availability. In any event, low-level modulation finds favor in many applications.

It has been widely employed in such diverse services as radio broadcasting and in amateur radio communications. It is used in television transmitters because the requisite wide-band techniques would involve greater technical and economic problems at high than at low power levels. Even when a station has previously operated at high-level modulation, the easiest and least costly method of increasing power is by the addition of a linear amplifier. Such an amplifier boosts the power level of an already modulated carrier. This constitutes low-level modulation from a system viewpoint.

As with high-level modulation, the ideal performance of a low-level modulated system corresponds to a linear modulating capability of 100 percent. Such capability may seldom be exploited. However, its attainment is always a worthwhile design approach. On the other hand, certain transmitters are operated as close to sustained 100 percent modulation as possible.

Operation of Low- and High-Level Modulated Amplifiers

Table 3-1 and Table 3-2 compare the operations of low-level modulated and high-level modulated amplifiers. The comparison of Table 3-1 is made on the basis of equal output power of the modulated carrier. The comparison of Table 3-2 is made on the basis of performance attained when the same tube and same power supply is used.

Referring to Table 3-1, note that the average plate efficiency during the modulation cycle of the low-level modulated amplifier is not the 37½ percent listed as the efficiency without modulation. The average efficiency during the modulation cycle is calculated

Table 3-1. Low- and High-Level Modulation Compared on the Basis of Obtaining the Same Power Output

Low-Level Modulated Amplifier*	Operating Parameter	High-Level Modulated Amplifier*
100 watts	output without modulation	100 watts
37.5%	plate efficiency without modulation	75%
266.7 watts	input without modulation	133.3 watts
75%	plate efficiency at crest of modulating cycle	75%
400 watts	output at crest of modulating cycle	400 watts
533.3 watts	input at crest of modulating cycle	533.3 watts
0%	plate efficiency at trough of modulating cycle	75%
0 watts	output at trough of modulating cycle	0 watts
0 watts	input at trough of modulating cycle	0 watts
56.2%	average plate efficiency during modulation cycle	75%
266.7 watts	average input during modulation cycle	200 watts
150 watts	average output during modulation cycle	150 watts
Several watts	modulating power required	66.6 watts

*100% sine-wave modulation.

Table 3-2. Low- and High-Level Modulation Compared on the Basis of Using the Same Tube and the Same Power Supply

Low-Level Modulated Amplifier*	Operating Parameter	High-Level Modulated Amplifier*
100 watts	output without modulation	400 watts
37.5%	plate efficiency without modulation	75%
266.7 watts	input without modulation	533.3 watts
75%	plate efficiency at crest of modulating cycle	75%
400 watts	output at crest of modulating cycle	1600 watts
533.3 watts	input at crest of modulating cycle	2133 watts
0%	plate efficiency at trough of modulating cycle	75%
0 watts	output at trough of modulating cycle	0 watts
0 watts	input at trough of modulating cycle	0 watts
56.2%	average plate efficiency during modulation cycle	75%
266.7 watts	average input during modulating cycle	800 watts
150 watts	average output during modulating cycle	600 watts
Several watts	modulating power required	266.6 watts

*100% sine-wave modulation.

as follows: The average output during the modulation cycle is known quite apart from the fact that low-level modulation is being used. From basic amplitude-modulation principles, the power content of a completely modulated wave is 1½ times that of the unmodulated carrier. Thus, average output in our case is 150 watts. Inasmuch as the efficiency of any device is the ratio of its output to its input, the next step is to determine the average input power during modulation. We recall that no variation of power input takes place in low-level modulation. Therefore, we may obtain the value of this constant input power by simply dividing the stipulated output of 100 watts by the efficiency which prevails without modulation. Thus, $100/37.5 = 266.7$ watts. This is both the input without modulation and the average input during the modulation cycle. Now having the values of average input and output during modulation, the average efficiency is computed as the ratio of the latter to the former. Thus $150/266.7 = 56.2$ percent. This is the average operating plate efficiency of our low-level modulated amplifier under the condition of sustained 100 percent sine-wave modulation. At the crest of the modulating sine wave, the efficiency is 75 percent. At the trough of the modulating sine wave, the efficiency is zero. Note that the average efficiency during modulation is 1½ times the efficiency with no modulation. Conversely during high-level modulation the efficiency remains constant at 75 per cent.

GRID MODULATION

Grid modulation can be accomplished in a number of ways. In a triode, one grid, the control grid, is used to accomplish modulation. A tetrode has the control grid and an additional grid, the screen grid, both of which may be used to modulate. A pentode has an additional grid called the suppressor grid. All of these grids can be used for modulating purposes.

Control-Grid Modulation

Control-grid modulation, also known as grid-bias modulation, typifies low-level, variable-efficiency modulation. This amplitude-modulation technique is one of the oldest of the communications art, having had extensive use in radio broadcast transmitters. It has also been widely employed by radio amateurs. A quick insight into the modulating mechanism involved is provided by considering a class-C r-f amplifier with appropriate d-c operating voltages and r-f excitation so that optimum power is delivered into the antenna or other load. Assume that grid bias is derived from a power supply

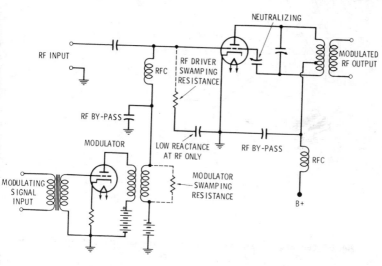

Fig. 3-4. Basic control grid modulation circuit.

with provision for manual control of its voltage. If, now, the d-c grid bias is made increasingly negative, the r-f power output of the amplifier will decrease. At a sufficiently high negative grid bias, the r-f power output will become zero. This behavior results from the fact that less of the positive half-cycle of the r-f excitation is able to penetrate the cutoff bias value as fixed bias is made progressively more negative. At sufficiently high negative grid bias, the amplitude of positive half-cycles of r-f excitation is no longer able to produce plate current pulses. Accordingly, no output is developed across the resonant tank in the plate circuit. This experiment suggests in a qualitative way that amplitude modulation can be produced in the plate circuit by varying the grid bias at the modulating signal rate. A basic circuit arrangement for accomplishing such amplitude modulation is shown in Fig. 3-4.

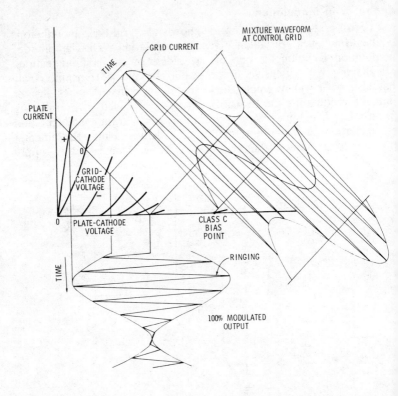

MIXTURE WAVEFORM
AT CONTROL GRID

GRID CURRENT

TIME

PLATE
CURRENT

GRID-
CATHODE
VOLTAGE

0   PLATE-CATHODE
VOLTAGE

CLASS C
BIAS
POINT

RINGING

TIME

100% MODULATED
OUTPUT

Fig. 3-5. Control-grid modulation of a triode illustrated with plate characteristics and load line.

In order to secure good results from such modulation, d-c grid bias, r-f excitation, and the superimposed modulating signal must be related as shown in Figs. 3-5 and 3-6. Fig. 3-5 shows the plate characteristics of a tube and load line with the mixture wave impressed along the control-grid voltage axis. Plate current pulses may be obtained from the points on the load line corresponding to the proper control-grid voltage. Fig. 3-6 shows the basic grid modulation circuit and illustrates how the grid voltage (e_g) is derived. If this hypothetical tube has a plate supply voltage of 20 volts, then a plate voltage wave form (e_p) may be drawn as shown. It may be seen from the waveform that at the 100 percent modula-

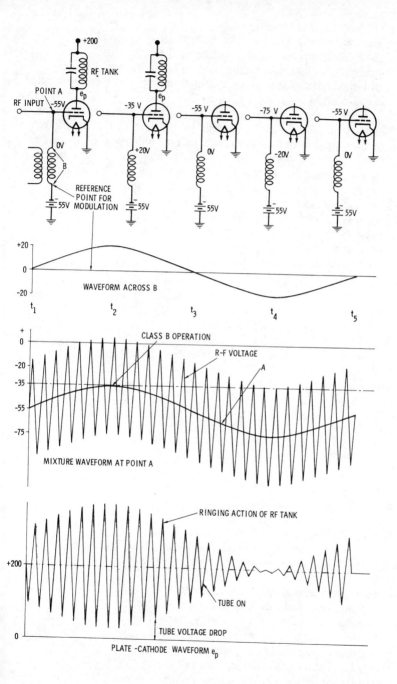

Fig.3-6. Control-grid modulation

tion peak (time t_2) the tube voltage drop is small, indicating high plate efficiency. However, at time t_1 the tube voltage drop is large, indicating a low plate efficiency. The difference between control-grid modulation and plate modulation may be seen by comparing Fig. 3-6 and Fig. 2-10 in Chapter 2.

At the crest of 100 percent modulation, the tube operates as a class-B amplifier. This is evident by the fact that plate current conduction at this time corresponds to one half-cycle of the r-f excitation. For other portions of the modulating cycle, the tube operates as an underexcited class-C amplifier. The excitation delivered to the grid of a class-C amplifier governs its plate efficiency in a manner such as shown in Fig. 3-7. Thus, the modulating cycle of a grid-modulated class-C amplifier varies both its plate current and its plate efficiency. One of the effects of modulating the value of the grid bias is similar to what would be produced if the excitation amplitude was varied. Summing up actual operating conditions, the

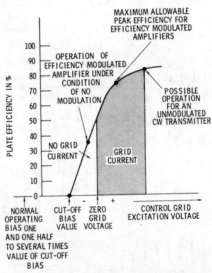

Fig. 3-7. Plate efficiency versus control-grid excitation voltage in a grid-modulated class-C r-f amplifier.

tube is operated with fixed excitation and fixed bias. These two parameters establish half maximum-efficiency class-C operation in a midway region of the grid voltage versus plate-current transfer curve so that reasonable linearity can be obtained when the superimposed modulating signal sweeps the operational mode down to zero efficiency and up to twice the no-modulation efficiency. Under the latter condition, operation is class-B wherein plate current conduction prevails throughout one-half of the carrier cycle.

The general ideas pertaining to control grid modulation are applicable to screen-grid modulation, suppressor-grid modulation, and to the linear amplifier. These efficiency-modulated amplifiers will be subsequently discussed.

Two sources of nonlinear modulation manifest themselves in practical grid-modulated amplifiers. One is that the requirement for constant-amplitude carrier excitation is difficult to meet throughout the modulating cycle. As the modulating signal approaches its crest, the grid-modulated amplifier undergoes the transition from no grid current to heavy grid current. Thus, the grid impedance changes from a very high value to a relatively low value. Unless the driver stage has exceedingly good output regulation, its r-f voltage will diminish in amplitude with the increased loading presented to it with increasing grid current. Nonlinear modulation will then result. In order to counteract such nonlinearity, a swamping resistance is often inserted in the grid circuit. When a tuned input tank is used, the swamping resistance is placed across it, or across appropriate taps. Of course, the Q of this tank is degraded and more excitation power is needed from the driver. However, driver regulation is greatly improved because the impedance variations of the modulated amplifier grid circuit no longer constitute the entire or even the major portion of the load presented to the driver. Control-grid modulated tetrodes and pentodes make less imposition on driver regulation.

A second source of nonlinearity involves a similar variable load effect with respect to the modulator. Here, a resistive load placed across the modulating transformer swamps out much of the impedance variation of the grid circuit. Of course, this now means added power capability on the part of the modulator. This generally is not objectionable because the modulating power still remains a small fraction of that required for high-level modulation. Usually, a modulator for grid modulation will have sufficient reserve power capability to enable a good measure of swamping. Both of these swamping resistors are shown in Fig. 3-4.

When exceedingly good modulating linearity is desired, it is feasible to adjust the operating parameters so that grid current never flows. This has been done in broadcast transmitters. Selection of an appropriate tube then becomes important from the standpoint of avoiding excessive loss in average operating efficiency.

One of the disadvantages of grid modulation is the somewhat critical nature of the adjustment procedure. For example, excessive r-f grid excitation or insufficient output loading can very easily project operation into distortion regions. An oscilloscope should always be used to monitor the effect on modulating linearity of any changes.

Suppressor-Grid Modulation

A representative suppressor-grid modulation circuit is shown in Fig. 3-8. An r-f pentode with externally terminated suppressor grid is required. The modulation is applied to the suppressor grid in similar fashion to modulation injection in the control-grid modulated amplifier. The operation is very much like that of control-grid modulation. As shown in Fig. 3-9, sufficient negative bias is impressed on the suppressor grid to reduce output carrier current to one-half of the amplitude which would be obtained with the suppressor grid at ground potential. With such bias, the plate efficiency of the tube is also one-half of the value corresponding to grounded-suppressor operation. On 100 percent modulation crests, both output carrier current and plate efficiency are doubled, thus quadrupling the peak power. As in other modulating methods, the average value of d-c plate current does not vary with modulation. With sine-wave modulation and a linear relation between modulating-signal voltage and modulation-envelope amplitude, a d-c ammeter in the B-plus power supply lead will show no deflection.

With some tubes, particularly the larger ones, it is necessary to drive the suppressor grid positive in order to bring about 100 percent modulation. During recent years tube manufacturers have concentrated their efforts on beam-power tetrodes rather than large radio-frequency pentodes. However, within the domain of tube

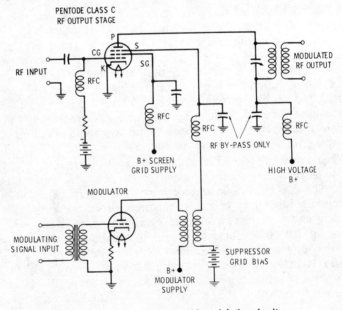

Fig. 3-8. Basic suppressor-grid modulation circuit.

availability, suppressor-grid modulation merits consideration as a low-level modulation tehnique. One of the advantages of this arrangement is that adjustment is appreciably less critical than is the case with control-grid modulation. This is due to the injection of carrier and modulating signals in conductively isolated circuits in the suppressor-grid modulated amplifier. Also, when the suppressor grid is not driven positive, virtually no modulating power is required.

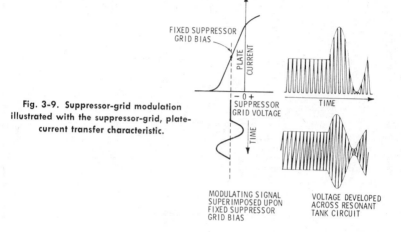

Fig. 3-9. Suppressor-grid modulation illustrated with the suppressor-grid, plate-current transfer characteristic.

A difficulty accompanying suppressor-grid modulation is inordinately high screen-grid current due to deflection by the negative suppressor of electrons from the vicinity of the plate to the screen grid. At worst, this necessitates operation at a lower power level. At best, it is found that the screen-grid dissipation limits the power input before the plate. Electron emission from an overheated screen grid can degrade modulation linearity. Thus, amateurs have found that it is not easy to "push" suppressor-grid modulated pentodes.

Screen-Grid Modulation

Screen-grid modulation is also similar to control-grid modulation. One method of accomplishing screen-grid modulation is shown in Fig. 3-10. Here, too, both plate current and plate efficiency vary linearly with the modulating signal voltage. The net result is that the r-f voltage developed across the output tank is directly proportional to the modulating voltage. It is not easy to achieve both good linearity and complete modulation with this method. On the other hand, the application of carrier and modulating signals to separate tube elements tends to make the adjustment of the screen-grid modulated amplifier easier than that of the control-grid modulated amplifier. Because of this, it is often found in practice that little disparity exists between the two methods if modulating quality is used as the basis of comparison. Satisfactory results are forthcoming from many tubes with grid-leak control-grid bias. Certainly, there is more latitude here than with control-grid modulation.

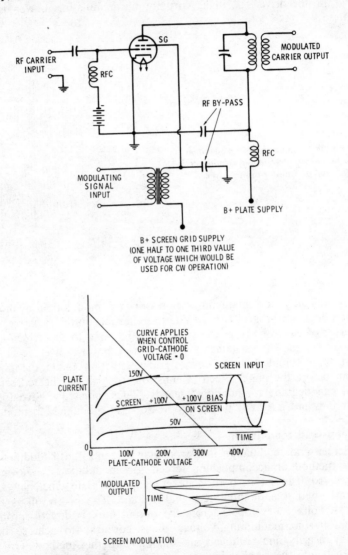

Fig. 3-10. Basic screen-grid modulation circuit using transformer coupling.

Like the control-grid modulated amplifier, carrier output amplitude is reduced to one-half of that which will prevail for 100 percent modulation peaks. This is brought about primarily by adjustment of the d-c screen-grid voltage. However, modulating linearity will not be approached unless attention is also paid to r-f excitation of the control grid. Tight antenna loading is also required. Beam-power tetrodes perform considerably better as screen-grid modulated amplifiers than do pentodes. In order to achieve complete envelope modulation, it is generally necessary to drive the screen grid negative. This presents the modulator with a widely varying load impedance. In order to prevent distortion from the modulator itself, it is very desirable that the modulator output impedance be low. This can be accomplished by appropriate feedback paths in the modulator and speech amplifier, by a step-down modulating transformer, or by a dummy load. Such techniques will increase the power requirement for the modulator, but not excessively.

Four efficiency-modulated tubes would have to be connected in parallel, or in push-pull parallel, in order to produce the power output obtainable from one tube in high-level modulated service. This is true for control-grid modulation, suppressor-grid modulation, and screen-grid modulation. However, the modulator power requirement would still remain very much less for all of these efficiency-modulated schemes than for the high-level modulated tube. In practice, another fact helps reduce the disparity between carrier-amplifier tube deployment in high-and low-level modulation. It often happens that a tube may be limited in terms of peak current, peak voltage, or peak power rather than by average plate dissipation. When this is so, it is no longer true that four times the modulated carrier power can be generated in high-level modulation with respect to low-level modulation. Thus, a screen-grid modulated tube may produce half of the power it could safely handle if it were high-level modulated. These considerations often make the low-level modulation schemes compare more favorably with high-level modulation.

A cathode-follower modulator is well suited for the requirements of screen-grid modulation. Such a circuit is shown in Fig. 3-11. This modulator has both the requisite low output impedance and excellent class-A linearity. The elimination of the modulating transformer helps conserve space and weight in mobile systems.

The use of a clamp tube provides yet another method of producing screen-grid modulation. In the circuit shown in Fig. 3-12, the resemblance to Heising plate modulation can be seen. Here, the screen grid resistor R2 substitutes for the conventional modulation choke in the Heising plate-modulation system. This is practical because the d-c screen-grid current is relatively low compared to

d-c plate current. Also, R2 serves the useful purpose of dropping the quiescent d-c screen-grid voltage to a value below that of plate voltage. In order to achieve full modulation capability, the plate voltage of the modulator tube must be higher than the screen-grid voltage of the modulated amplifier. This is brought about by resistance R2 which is bypassed for the lowest involved modulating frequency. A popular modulating tube has been the 6Y6. This tube is connected to operate essentially as a class-A triode by typing its screen grid to its plate. The modulated amplifier is an 807, 6146, or similar beam-power pentode. The modulator tube must be provided with fixed grid bias in order that its class-A operating point will not shift with modulation. On the other hand, the deletion of the fixed bias can profitably be used to purposely cause the carrier output level to swing up and down with the modulation factor. This is so-called controlled carrier operation. It is then necessary to impose an RC time constant in the 6Y6 input circuit so that carrier output level is governed by the average, rather than instantaneous, amplitude of the modulating voltage. A better means of accomplishing controlled carrier operation is described in Chapter 4. In the discussion covering balanced modulators, the circuit of Fig. 3-27 is that of a balanced modulator with screen-grid modulation.

The suppressor-grid and screen-grid modulation schemes described make use of class-C pentode and tetrode amplifiers. This yields the highest output and plate efficiency and is therefore appropriate for transmitters. However, for instrumentation techniques it is well to realize that these two modulating methods also work well when the amplifier is operated class-A. This is not true for the other efficiency-modulating circuit, grid-bias modulation. A linear class-A amplifier cannot be grid modulated. The apparent exception is the van der Bijl modulator. This modulated amplifier is, in a manner of speaking, operated as a class-A amplifier. However. it has a dependency on a nonlinear segment of its transfer function. This operation is contrary to the conventional operation of class-A amplifiers where nonlinearity is either avoided or made to be a relatively small portion of the overall dynamic range.

CATHODE MODULATION

Cathode modulation incorporates characteristics of both high-level and low-level modulation. Inasmuch as the cathode circuit provides return paths for both input and output circuits of the modulated amplifier, modulation is intermediate between control-grid and plate modulation. The required modulating power depends on the relative percentages of grid and plate modulation. This is subject

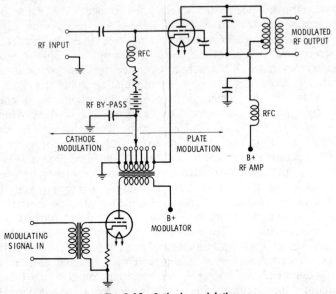

Fig. 3-13. Cathode modulation.

to adjustment by means of the tapped transformer shown in the cathode-modulation arrangement of Fig. 3-13. If the grid return is tapped at the cathode terminal of the modulation transformer, a condition of "pure" plate modulation will exist. The circuit configuration will then differ from the conventional plate-modulated amplifier only in that the modulation is introduced in the negative d-c supply lead rather than in the positive lead. This had no important consequence. Such operation would, of course, require a relatively powerful modulator and a husky modulation transformer.

On the other hand, if the grid-return tap is moved to the ground side of the modulation transformer, we will have cathode modulation with the highest selectable percentage of grid modulation possible with this circuit. It is found that optimum overall economy of operation occurs with a transformer tap providing about 40 percent plate modulation and 60 percent grid modulation. No provision is made for "pure" grid modulation with this arrangement. With the suggested 40 percent plate modulation, the modulator need supply only 40 percent of the power which would be required for pure plate modulation. In conjunction with this, the average efficiency of the cathode-modulated amplifier over the modulating cycle will be in the vicinity of 65 percent which is reasonably close to the 75 percent or so ordinarily had for pure plate modulation. Power output will be about halfway between that of pure plate and grid modulation.

The modulating impedance seen by the modulator of a cathode-modulated amplifier is $m \times E_p / I_p$. Here, m represents the modulation factor (plate modulation). E_p and I_p are respectively the plate voltage and plate current of the modulated amplifier. This is a practical design value, but the cathode impedance actually undergoes some variation during the modulating cycle. Therefore, the modulator

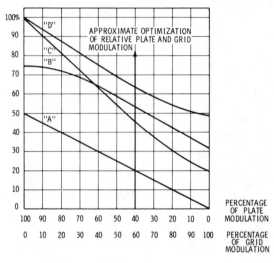

COMPARISON OF CATHODE MODULATION TO HIGH LEVEL
PLATE MODULATION OF SAME TUBE

"A" REQUIRED MODULATOR POWER AS PERCENTAGE OF ACTUAL
DC POWER INPUT

"B" PLATE EFFICIENCY PERCENTAGE

"C" CARRIER OUTPUT POWER AS PERCENTAGE OF THAT CORRES-
PONDING TO PURE PLATE MODULATION

"D" ACTUAL INPUT POWER AS PERCENTAGE OF THAT CORRES-
PONDING TO PURE PLATE MODULATION

**Fig. 3-14. Comparison of cathode modulation to high-level
plate modulation of same tube.**

should be stabilized by negative feedback. This circuit tends to aggravate the effects of crossover distortion in class-B modulators; it is better to operate the modulator tubes in class A or in class AB. Fig. 3-14 compares the operation of the cathode-modulated amplifier with that of pure plate modulation. In Fig. 3-14 100 percent modulation exists for all comparisons. Only the division of plate and grid modulation is varied. (This is done by varying the modulation transformer taps of Fig. 3-13).

On first thought, a quick and easy way to boost the power of an amplitude-modulated wave would be to design an appropriate class-C amplifier. This appears to be the proper approach when we contemplate the use of the class-C amplifier for both high-level and low-level modulation. Unfortunately, for most applications, such a tech-

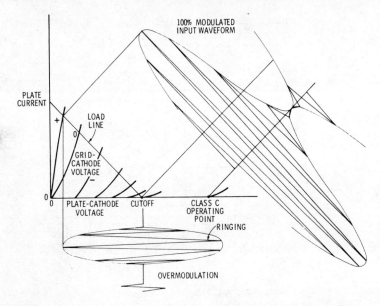

Fig. 3-15. Result of applying amplitude-modulated wave to class-C amplifier.

nique would prove disastrous. Fig. 3-15 illustrates the consequences when a class-C amplifier is excited with an amplitude-modulated wave. Although, the signal thereby applied to the input circuit is a 100 percent sinusoidally modulated wave, the output wave exhibits distortion and overmodulation. How this comes about is readily seen by graphical projection of the input wave with respect to the plate-current versus grid-voltage transfer curve of the tube.

The Class-B Linear Amplifier

If the tuned amplifier is operated in its class-B mode rather than its class-C mode, we achieve the conditions depicted in Fig. 3-16. In this case, it is obvious that it is possible to boost the power of an amplitude-modulated wave and retain its envelope characteristics. In other respects, the operation is similar to that of low-level modulation schemes such as is accomplished in grid-bias modulation. In much the same way, the class-B linear amplifier under-

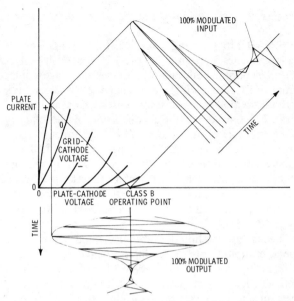

Fig. 3-16. Result of applying amplitude-modulated wave to class-B amplifier.

goes variation in plate efficiency with the modulating signal. At the crest of modulation, peak plate efficiency is attained. This has a theoretical upper limit of 78.5 percent. When there is no modulation, the plate efficiency is half the peak value. At the trough of the modulating cycle, plate efficiency is zero. At that time, both input and output are zero. Thus, the class-B linear amplifier is both plate-current and plate-efficiency modulated by the envelope of the applied amplitude-modulated wave.

From reasoning similar to that which prevails for the efficiency-modulated arrangements, such as grid-bias modulation, the class-B linear amplifier requires four tubes to provide the same power boost attainable from the same type of tube when high-level modulated. Often, however, the comparison is more favorable for the class-B linear amplifier. Tubes are sometimes limited in terms of peak plate voltage or peak input power. Comparing the two power-boost schemes in the opposite way now, this means that a given tube might not be able to safely develop four times as much power in high-level modulation service than as a class-B linear amplifier. Tubes are subjected to severe stresses in high-level modulation where peak values of twice unmodulated peak plate voltage and four times unmodulated power are demanded. In practice, class-B linear amplifiers often merit consideration when it is desired to increase the power output of a transmitter satisfactory in other respects. A compelling feature is that nothing need be changed in the modulating system.

Unlike class-B tubes in audio service, the class-B linear amplifier for radio frequencies need not be used in the push-pull configuration. The tuned output tank circuit provides the mirror image to the plate-current pulses, as with single-ended class-C amplifiers. The shape of the individual plate-current pulses is not as important as in audio work. The harmonics due to distortion of the plate pulses are multiples of the carrier frequency. They are outside the range of interest and are highly attenuated by the tuned tank. The most important operating feature of the linear amplifier is the linearity of the plate-current, grid-voltage transfer function. This obviously governs the fidelity of reproduction of the modulation envelope.

One of the practical difficulties encountered with class-B linear amplifiers is the effect on the driving stage when the grid draws current. The severe loading thereby presented tends to lower the peak-to-peak amplitude of the modulation envelope. This, of course, degrades linearity and constitutes distortion of the modulation. For this reason, efficiency is sometimes sacrificed for the sake of linearity by operating in the region between class-B and class-A. A particularly good compromise results from operation of r-f beam power tubes as class AB_1 linear amplifiers. Such operation consumes no grid current, provides linear amplification of the modulation envelope, and retains reasonable average plate efficiency. Another approach is to operate in class-B mode but in conjunction with a swamping resistance in the grid circuit. Such a resistance causes a relatively constant load to be imposed on the driver. Of course, the price exacted is the requirement of considerably more power from the driver stage. Considering the efficiency of both driver and linear amplifier, the class AB_1 mode of operation often proves the best approach to good linearity. When no grid current is consumed there is no need for the dissipative loading of a swamping resistance. Class-A linear amplifiers have been used with some of the older transmitting triodes. However, the peak plate efficiency theoretically attainable is then only 50 percent.

The grounded-grid configuration lends itself particularly well for linear operation. A representative circuit is shown in Fig. 3-17. This circuit is degenerative and very stable. Neutralization of triodes so used is needed only for the very highest frequencies. Radio-frequency beam-power pentodes such as the 807 and the 1625 require neither a grid-bias supply or a screen-grid power supply when operated as a grounded-grid linear amplifier. The screen grid is connected directly to r-f and d-c ground. The beam-forming plates should also be grounded. In some brands of these tubes it is necessary to remove the base and disconnect the lead from the beam-forming plates from

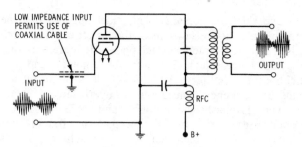

Fig. 3-17. Basic grounded-grid class-B linear amplifier.

the cathode lead. The 7094 is a higher-power beam-power tube. As a grounded-grid linear amplifier it is capable of delivering peak output power levels in the vicinity of 250 watts. To accomplish this, 15 watts of driving power is required. The driving power required by a grounded-grid amplifier is, for the greater part, not in the nature of a dissipative loss. Most of this power adds to the power developed in the output circuit. (On the other hand, such power "leak-through" makes the grounded-grid amplifier generally undesirable for service as a plate-modulated amplifier. The residual r-f power remaining in the output tank precludes the possibility of complete modulation when the d-c plate voltage is reduced to zero at the trough of the modulating cycle.)

SWITCHING MODULATORS

Switching modulators make use of the rectification properties of unilateral-conduction elements. One of the impressed signals is relatively large so that an approach to linear rectification is achieved in one direction and an open circuit in the other. Commonly encountered configurations employ four diodes. The basic circuits are shown in Fig. 3-18 and Fig. 3-20. This modulation technique produces a suppressed-carrier modulation spectrum. Suppressed-carrier transmission eliminates the power wastage in the noninformation bearing carrier. However, for the purpose of demodulation, an artificial carrier must be reinserted. This is very critical because both frequency and phase conditions must have stability if the reconstructed modulation envelope is to faithfully follow the original modulating signal. These switching modulators are found as the prelude to single-sideband transmission. Single-sideband communication displays a more reasonable tolerance with respect to carrier reinsertion. To convert the output from a switching modulator to single sideband, it is only necessary to employ appropriate filter selectivity to eliminate the undesired sideband. Inasmuch as the carrier has been "electronically" eliminated in the modulation pro-

113

cess, a single sideband remains. This sideband can then be hetero-dyned for ultimate use elsewhere in the spectrum. This technique is widely used in carrier-frequency telephony. It represents one method of producing single-sideband power for amateur and commercial radiotelephone transmitters. Additionally, it is often encountered as the means of frequency translation in superheterodyne communications receivers, primarily where double and triple conversion is used.

The suppressed-carrier modulation pattern produced by switching modulators of the balanced variety (such as the circuits of Fig. 3-18 and Fig. 3-20) provides an interesting contrast to the conventional amplitude-modulation pattern. This is revealed in the waveforms of Fig. 3-22. Note a basic difference between the patterns of Fig. 3-22C and Fig. 3-22D. In the latter, representing carrier suppression, there is an abrupt phase discontinuity. In the former, which is a conventional amplitude-modulation pattern, there is phase continuity. These switching modulators share in common with the balanced modulator, to be subsequently discussed, the suppression of the carrier component in the output circuit. The switching modulator generates considerably more modulation products in addition to this. Therefore, the desired performance of switching modulators is considerably dependent on subsequent filtering. For example, the bridge modulator of Fig. 3-20 generates very many sidebands. Moreover, the output also includes the original modulating frequency. This

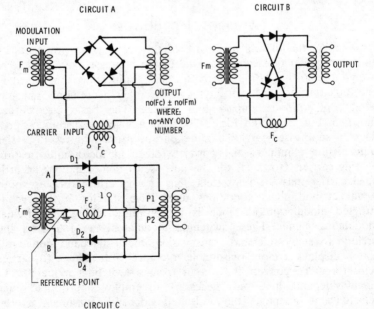

Fig. 3-18. Switching modulator: ring configuration.

could be anticipated by virtue of the direct connections between input and output transformers.

The ring configuration shown in Fig. 3-18 is also known as a double-balanced switching modulator. As implied, both modulating and carrier signals are balanced out. Filtering problems are considerably relaxed in this circuit. Not only is there no modulating signal to contend with in the output, but the modulation products include fewer extraneous sidebands than is the case with the bridge configuration.

Fig. 3-18 shows the ring modulator drawn in three different equivalent forms. Circuit C in Fig. 3-18 can best be used to illustrate the operation. The junction of the carrier voltage, F_c, and the center tap of the modulating transformer is the reference point from which the voltage waveforms will be taken. As shown in Fig. 3-19, the modulating voltages at points A and B are 180 degrees out of phase with each other, with respect to the reference point. The carrier voltage is applied to point 1. The output transformer pri-

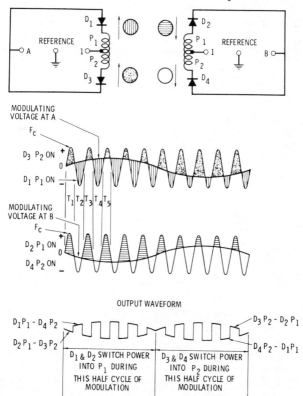

Fig. 3-19. Ring modulator operation.

mary is split into two coils, P1 and P2. The circuit is then redrawn into the two circuits shown in Fig. 3-19. One circuit has modulating voltage A applied to one end of a series-parallel circuit composed of D1, D3, P1, and P2. The second circuit has modulating voltage B applied to one end of a series-parallel circuit composed of D2, D4, P1, and P2. The carrier voltage F_c is applied to the junction of P1 and P2.

To show the relative polarity at any instant between the modulating voltage and the carrier voltage, they are drawn one over the other as shown in Fig. 3-19. Since there are two circuits, with the modulation voltage different in each, two waveform drawings are shown. Now it can be determined which diodes, connected between these voltages, are conducting during any given time interval.

For example, during time T_1 the modulating voltage A is less negative than the carrier F_c indicating that diode D3 is conducting current through coil P2. During the same time interval the modulating voltage at B is less negative than the carrier F_c, indicating that diode D2 is conducting current through coil P1. However, these currents are in opposite directions in the coil primary, and the output is a result of the difference between these currents. During time T_1 the output is due to the difference D2 P1 − D3 P2, since the D2 P1 circuit conducts more than the D3 P2 circuit. The shaded portions of the waveforms indicate which diodes are conducting during any time interval. The output, then, is the result of

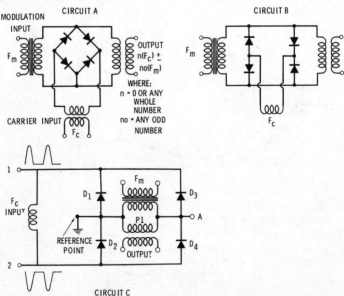

Fig. 3-20. Switching modulator: bridge configuration.

the diodes conducting current through the output coils and being switched at the carrier rate. During the first half-cycle of modulation the resultant output is caused by diodes D1 and D2 switching power into output coil P1, and during the second half-cycle of modulation the output is caused by diodes D3 and D4 switching power into output coil P2.

The bridge modulator is shown in Fig. 3-20 in three equivalent ways. Circuit C can be used to develop the operation of this modulator. Here, the reference point is the junction of diodes D1 and D2, and the modulation and output transformers. The modulating voltage is at A and is applied across output transformer P1. The carrier voltage is applied between points 1 and 2.

As shown in Fig. 3-20, the carrier voltage at point 1 with respect to the reference point is a positive half-wave. The carrier voltage at point 2 is a negative half-wave occurring at the same time that the voltage at point 1 is positive. Thus, the carrier voltages are 180 degrees out of phase with each other with respect to the reference point and are half-waves. These carrier voltages are plotted over the modulation voltage as before so as to determine which diode is on during any time interval.

Notice that when D1 and D2 are on and effectively shorting out the carrier voltage, D3 and D4 also perform the same function. Now, during the time interval T1, these diodes are all reversed biased and the modulation current has a path thru the output transformer P1.

Thus, an output pulse occurs during T1. During time interval T2 the diodes are conducting. The carrier voltage is shorted out and also the modulation voltage is shorted through D3, the low impedance carrier transformer, and D2. Then during this interval, no output occurs in P1. It can be seen from the waveforms that output occurs at the carrier rate during the first half of the modulation cycle due to nonconduction of D2 and D3. During the second half of the modulation cycle output occurs due to nonconduction of D1 and D4.

Therefore, although both configurations are switched at the carrier rate, the modulating signal is affected differently in the two cases. In the bridge type of switching modulator, the modulating signal is shorted out for one polarity of the carrier cycle and output occurs when the diodes are off. In the ring type of switching modulator, the modulating signal is alternately connected at the carrier rate across the output transformer in one way, then the other, causing an output when the diodes are on. The waveforms produced by the switching actions in the two configurations before filtering are shown in Fig. 3-22A and Fig. 3-22B. The output of both types after filtering is shown in Fig. 3-22D. Fig. 3-22C shows an a-m waveform for the purpose of comparison.

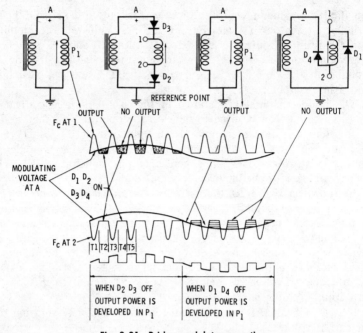

Fig. 3-21. Bridge modulator operation.

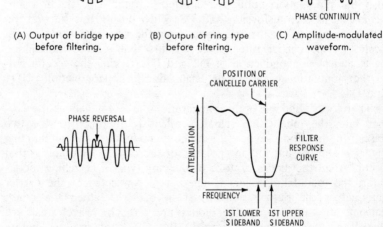

(A) Output of bridge type before filtering.

(B) Output of ring type before filtering.

(C) Amplitude-modulated waveform.

(D) Output of both types after filtering.

Fig. 3-22. Switching-modulator waveforms.

Note that despite the diamond arrangement of four diodes, the actual diode polarization is not the same in the two switching modulators. The bridge type of Fig. 3-20 employs the diodes in the same connection conventional to rectifying circuits. The ring type of Fig. 3-18 has the diodes "chasing" one another so as to suggest a closed ring. Nonobservance of these facts is one of the chief troubles encountered in first attempts in laboratory breadboard operation.

Not only can these switching modulators be utilized to transmit in either direction, but they can provide demodulation as well as modulation. Originally, they were made up from copper-oxide rectifying diodes. For the purposes of carrier telephony, excellent performance was obtained, particularly with respect to balance stability.

SQUARE-LAW MODULATION

In the transfer function of many devices, it is quite common to encounter a unique curvature for certain ranges of applied signals; it is found that a portion of the total output versus input curve can be utilized to provide a square-law relationship. This generally manifests itself with output current being proportional to the square of input voltage. Such devices produce amplitude modulation as the consequence of carrier and modulating signals interacting within

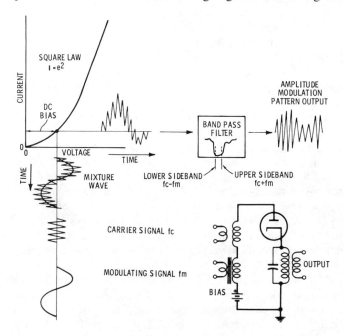

Fig. 3-23. Square-law modulation.

the square-law region of the transfer characteristic. This is graphically depicted in Fig. 3-23. The modulation products thereby generated from this square-law region are described mathematically by the following equation:

$$i = \frac{aE_c^2}{2} + \frac{aE_m^2}{2} + bE_c \sin \omega t + bE_m \sin qt$$

$$- aE_cE_m \cos (\omega + q) t + aE_cEm \cos(\omega - q)t$$

$$- \frac{aE_c^2}{2} \cos 2 \omega t - \frac{aE_m^2}{2} \cos 2qt$$

where,

i represents the total output current,
a and b are coefficients from the trigonometric derivation.
For the avowed purposes of identifying the modulation products, we need not concern ourselves with these coefficients,
E_c is the peak amplitude of the carrier signal,
E_m is the peak value of the modulating signal,
ω is 2π times the carrier frequency,
q is 2π times the modulating frequency.

Now, let us see what this equation informs us concerning the modulating properties of a square-law device. We note that there are eight separate terms. The first two terms combine to provide the d-c component resulting, one might say, from partial rectification of the applied signals. The third term $bE_c \sin \omega t$ is the carrier signal. The fourth term $bE_m \sin qt$ is the modulating signal. The fifth term is that of a sine wave with a frequency equal to the sum of the carrier-signal frequency and the modulating-signal frequency. Accordingly, the fifth term is the *upper sideband* of an ampltiude-modulated wave. The sixth term is that of a sine wave with a frequency equal to the carrier frequency minus the modulating frequency. Therefore, the sixth term is the *lower sideband* of an amplitude-modulated wave. More specifically, the fifth and sixth terms are the sidebands with respect to the carrier frequency described by the third term. The seventh term is the second harmonic of the carrier frequency. Finally, the eighth term is the second harmonic of the modulating frequency. A little thought reveals the possibility of useful results from this apparent bedlam of output frequencies.

We see that the retention of the third, fifth, and sixth terms and the rejection of all other terms leaves us with the spectrum of an amplitude-modulated wave. Fortunately, this is readily accomplished in practice with relatively simple bandpass filters. The resultant amplitude modulation is linear in the accepted sense that the *modulation envelope* varies in amplitude in direct proportion to the amplitude of the modulating signal. Somewhat paradoxically, linear amplitude-modulation has been achieved by means of a non-linear device. However, if the transfer curve is more violent than that described by the square law, distortion of the modulation envelope will occur. Such distortion is not readily removed by filters when modulation encompasses a wide band of frequencies, as in speech. On the other hand, if the device exhibits a gentler curve than that corresponding to the square-law relationship, linear modulation will result, but at shallower depth than may be attained for square-law operation. Even under ideal conditions pertaining to a true square-law relationship, this modulating technique suffers from low-modulating factors. However, it is feasible in practical circuits to secure good linearity by careful attention to transfer curvature.

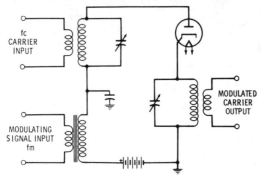

Fig. 3-24. Diode square-law modulator.

Fig. 3-24 shows a diode square-law modulator. Semiconductor diodes are similarly applicable. Where the modulating objective is frequency translation of a single modulating signal, it is often practical to dispense with the d-c bias. Considerable departure from the square-law relationship is not of great significance for this purpose. For speech modulation, it is worthwhile to optimize the d-c bias as well as the amplitudes of carrier and modulating signals for minimum distortion of the amplitude-modulated output.

A triode tube may be used to provide square-law modulation with two advantages over the diode circuit. The input impedance of the triode, when so employed, is very high over the total excursions of both carrier and modulating signals. Therefore, a source of distortion is eliminated. In the diode circuit, the carrier and modulating-signal sources are exposed to a relatively low and varying impedance. This renders difficult the application of constant-amplitude signals as demanded for distortionless operation. The effect of such variation is to make the transfer relationship something other than that described by the square law. The second dividend obtained from the use of the triode tube is *power gain*.

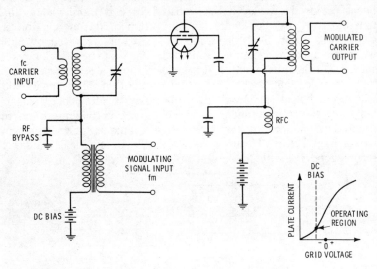

Fig. 3-25. The van der Bijl triode modulator.

Fig. 3-25 is the circuit of the van der Bijl triode modulator. The triode is operated in the lower region of its transfer curve relating plate current to grid voltage. Here we have a class-A amplifier in which a certain type of distortion is deliberately sought. As with the diode arrangement, linear amplitude-modulation occurs with true square-law operation. Interestingly, what would comprise severe distortion for conventional class-A amplifier performance enables the accomplishment of distortionless amplitude-modulation in the van der Bijl modulator. The circuit bears a resemblence to the grid-modulated class-C amplifier. However, it should be realized that the operation is altogether different. In the van der Bijl modulator, the tube does not function as a carrier-operated switch, and there is no shock-excitation of the resonant tank in the plate circuit. In the van der Bijl modulator the tube is not effectively used for production of rating-determined power levels. Accordingly, this modulator is found in such applications as carrier telephony and instrumentation.

THE BALANCED MODULATOR

The terminology "balanced modulator" most often applies to a back-to-back arrangement of twin van der Bijl modulators. The important feature of this configuration is its ability to provide double-sideband, suppressed-carrier modulation. This is very useful for many techniques. It often is the first step in a system of frequency translation. One method of producing single-sideband transmission makes use of the balanced modulator to simultaneously achieve modulation and carrier suppression. Thereafter the desired sideband is obtained by means of appropriate filter selectivity. Also, double-sideband, suppressed-carrier transmission has been used. For this type of modulation, the balanced modulator is directly applicable. Receiving and demodulating the suppressed-carrier transmission presents a unique difficulty, for it is found that the missing carrier must be reinserted prior to demodulation. Reinsertion requires considerable precision with respect to both frequency or phase. If either of these two parameters is not a replica of the original carrier, the reproduced-amplitude modulation envelope will be distorted. One solution has been to transmit a pilot frequency along with the two sidebands. Paradoxically, much greater tolerance attends the carrier-reinsertion technique for single-sideband communications. Moreover, single sideband achieves even higher efficiency in the matter of bandwidth requirement for the same modulating information. This is because ordinary amplitude modulation is redundant to begin with; either sideband serves to convey all of the modulating information. In any event, the balanced modulator is almost certain to be found in modulating systems with sophistication somewhat exceeding that just sufficing for the essentials of ordinary amplitude modulation.

The schematic diagram of a balanced modulator is shown in Fig. 3-26. Options are provided for operation in different modes. Fig. 3-26 also lists the modulation products resulting from different combinations of carrier and modulation injection as well as different output derivations. First, directing out attention to arrangement No. 1, we see that the output No. 2 consists of the carrier and the upper and lower sidebands. Thus, the balanced modulator is capable of producing conventional amplitude modulation. It is significant that this is accomplished without need of subsequent filtering. If square-law operation and electrical balance exist, the amplitude-modulation spectrum will be free of extraneous sidebands or harmonics. In actual practice, it is generally found expedient to tune the output transformer to the carrier frequency when the balanced modulator is so used. The Q of this resonant circuit should not be sufficiently high to attenuate the sidebands. Also, the transformer shown for output option No. 1 should, under

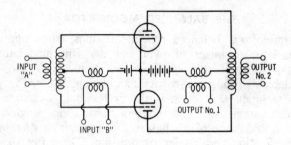

ARRANGEMENT	INPUTS		OUTPUTS		OPERATIONAL FEATURE
	A	B	No. 1	No. 2	
1	f_c	f_m	f_m, $2f_m$, $2f_c$	f_c, $f_c - f_m$, $f_c + f_m$	CARRIER PLUS TWO SIDEBANDS AT OUTPUT No. 2
2	f_m	f_c	f_c, $2f_m$, $2f_c$	f_m, $f_c - f_m$, $f_c + f_m$	SUPPRESSED CARRIER AT OUTPUT No. 2
3	$f_m + f_c$	0	$2f_c$, $2f_m$, $f_c - f_m$, $f_c + f_m$	f_c, f_m	SUPPRESSED CARRIER AT OUTPUT No. 1

f_c REPRESENTS THE HIGHER IMPRESSED FREQUENCY.
f_m REPRESENTS THE LOWER IMPRESSED FREQUENCY.

Fig. 3-26. Balanced modulator.

this operating condition, be replaced by a direct connection. Such an amplitude modulator is very useful for low-power applications.

In arrangement No. 2, we encounter the carrier-suppression property of the balanced modulator. The modulation products appearing at output option No. 2 comprise the modulating signal and the upper and lower sidebands of the suppressed carrier. By tuning the output transformer to the frequency of the suppressed carrier, the two sidebands will still be available (providing the Q of the resonant tank is not too high), but the modulating frequency will be attenuated to a negligible level. When used for suppressed-carrier modulation in this way, the transformer for output option No. 1 should be replaced by a direct connection.

In arrangement No. 3 different input and output options are used in order to again accomplish suppressed-carrier modulation. The modulation products are now derived from output option No. 1. The modulation products comprise the second harmonic of the carrier, the second harmonic of the modulating signal, and the upper and lower sidebands of the suppressed-carrier frequency.

Here again, if we tune the output transformer to the carrier frequency, the two adjacent sidebands will constitute the output of the modulator. The near-resonant transformer will offer high impedance to these near-carrier frequencies. Other modulation products will encounter low impedance and thereby be virtually short-circuited. When the balanced modulator is operated in this mode, the output transformer used for option No. 2 should be replaced by direct connections. Likewise, the input transformer used for input option B should be replaced by a direct connection. The choice between arrangements No. 2 and No. 3 depends considerably on the closeness of the carrier frequency to the highest modulating frequency. Where these approach one another too closely, it may not be easy to reject the two unwanted modulation products ($2f_c$ and $2f_m$) of arrangement No. 3. Also, arrangement No. 3 offers no provision for separate carrier and modulating-signal inputs.

The carrier-suppressing feature of the balanced modulator is retained even if the tubes depart from square-law operation. Indeed, the basic idea is even applicable to class-C operation. When the transfer function of the tubes is more violent than that of the square-law relation, more modulation products and more harmonics will be generated. On the other hand, when the nonlinearity of the transfer function is more gentle than that described by the square law, the already low operating efficiency of this circuit will be further degraded.

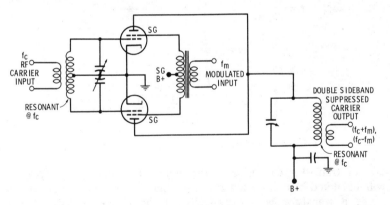

Fig. 3-27. A balanced modulator using screen-grid modulation.

The circuit of Fig. 3-27 is that of a balanced modulator using screen-grid modulation. The use of separate tube elements is advantageous in that modulating and carrier frequencies are considerably restricted from entering circuit sections of the system where they do not belong. In other respects, the suppressed-carrier output is produced by a similar process to that of the triode balanced modulator of Fig. 3-26 under the output condition No. 1 stipulated in arrangement No. 3 in Table in Fig. 3-26. The carrier signal is injected into push-pull control grids. The modulating signal is applied to push-pull screen grids. Suppression of both the carrier signal and the modulating signal takes place in the output circuit because the plates of the two tetrodes are connected in parallel. This basic circuit has been extensively used in the single-sideband transmitters designed around the "filter" system approach. Screen-grid modulation is not dependent on square-law or any other type of nonlinearity. Relatively efficient performance is obtained with control grid, screen grid, and plate all operating within linear dynamic ranges. The circuit operates as a class-A amplifier with two inputs.

LOW-LEVEL MODULATION WITH TRANSISTORS

Fig. 3-28 and Fig. 3-29 show transistor counterparts of "grid" and "cathode" tube modulation techniques. Good linearity is not readily forthcoming from these modulation schemes due to the varia-

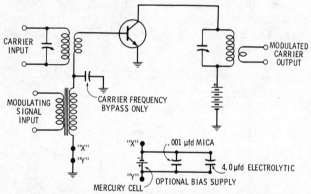

Fig. 3-28. Transistor counterpart of grid-bias modulation.

tion of transistor current gain throughout the modulating cycle. It will be noted that no fixed d-c base bias is indicated. This is because a transistor is automatically in the class-BC region when zero-biased. With some transistors, linearity will be improved if a small additional source of reverse base-emitter bias is inserted in the base-return lead. Such a bias source must provide a low d-c voltage, say from one-half of a volt to about two volts, but must constitute a very low impedance. A mercury cell bypassed by a 0.001-mfd mica capacitor as well as a 4-mfd electrolytic capacitor has been found satisfactory for a number of experimental amplifiers investigated by the author. In both circuits, the modulating transformer will have a step-down ratio looking into the modulated transistor stage. This is best determined experimentally.

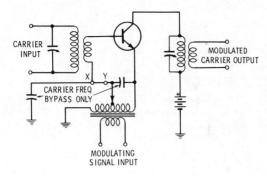

Fig. 3-29. Transistor counterpart of cathode modulation.

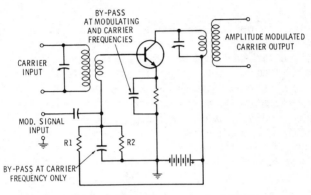

Fig. 3-30. Low-level modulation using base injection.

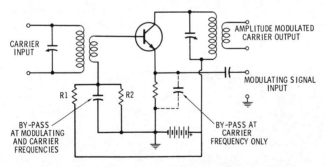

Fig. 3-31. Low-level modulation using emitter injection.

The two circuits depicted in Fig. 3-30 and Fig. 3-31 are schematically somewhat similar to those described previously. However, the operating modes of these modulated transistor amplifiers are quite different. In these two circuits, the transistors are forward-biased with very small emitter-base current. When so biased,

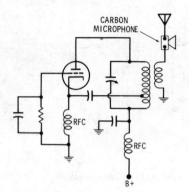

Fig. 3-32. Absorption modulation of low-power oscillator.

transistors develop collector-circuit voltage gain which is linearly dependent on base-emitter current. If a modulating signal is superimposed on the small emitter-base current, both collector voltage and collector current will be varied so as to produce a fairly linear amplitude-modulation envelope across the output tank. The power levels generated by these circuits are very much lower than those obtainable from the circuits of Fig. 3-28 and Fig. 3-29. It can be appreciated that even the class-A capabilities of the transistors are not effectively utilized. On the other hand, these circuits are less demanding of carrier excitation and modulation power than the "grid" and "cathode" modulation arrangements of Fig. 3-28 and Fig. 3-29. The circuits of Fig. 3-30 and Fig. 3-31 are applicable to the requirements of wireless microphones, phonograph oscillators, toys, and instrumentation techniques. The low-level modulation schemes of Fig. 3-28 and Fig. 3-29 have more relevant applicability to small transmitters and elsewhere power output is important.

ABSORPTION MODULATION

In the older literature, one finds radiotelephone transmission predicated on such techniques as shown in Fig. 3-32. Here, a single-button carbon microwave is inserted directly in the antenna lead of a low-power oscillator. Modulation is accomplished by voice-dependent variance of the microphone resistance. Of course, such a "losser" modulation method is crude, primitive, and incapable of good performance. However, absorption modulation is by no means obsolete. The circuit of Fig. 3-32 may be improved in some respects. A master oscillator-power amplifier arrangement would involve less frequency modulation. When used with transistors, a very inexpensive modulating technique is obtained for toys, phonograph oscillators, and certain instrumentation applications.

More recently, absorption modulation has been revived for a sophisticated application in microwave technology. A special *pin* diode* is inserted within a waveguide so as to either intercept or reflect an appreciable amount of microwave energy. When a modulating signal is impressed across the pin diode its forward resistance varies in accordance with the modulation. This, in turn, inflicts varying attenuation on the impinging microwave energy in such a way that an amplitude modulation is produced. This is an excellent way to video-modulate microwave power, inasmuch as the *pin* diode has very-high-frequency capabilities.

The *pin* diode is so designated because it contains a layer of *intrinsic* silicon between its p and n regions. This intrinsic semiconductor region stores sufficient charge so that diode rectification action ceases for frequencies beyond 100 megacycles. Rather, the device then behaves as a nonpolar variable resistance to such frequencies. Although this behavior is considered undesirable for many diode-dependent techniques, such as fast switching, it can be profitably used for absorption modulation of uhf and microwave energy. The nonpolar resistance which the *pin* diode presents to such high frequencies is inversely proportional to the amplitude of its forward bias. Thus, by modulating the bias, the r-f absorption property is varied accordingly. It should be appreciated that the device appears as a diode to direct current and modulating frequencies, but simultaneously as a nonpolar resistance to the high-frequency r-f energy. Fig. 3-33 is a partial block diagram illustrating the use of pin diodes to modulate high-frequency r-f signals in a transmission line. The number of diodes used and the inclusion of fixed resistances depend on r-f impedance-match considerations and power levels.

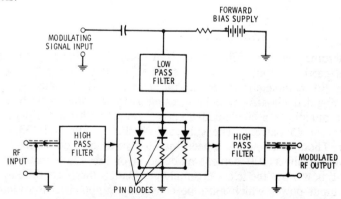

Fig. 3-33. Use of pin diodes to accomplish absorption modulation of r-f energy in a transmission line.

*Manufactured by HP Associates, Palo Alto, California

Chapter 4

TECHNIQUES FOR IMPROVING AMPLITUDE-MODULATION PERFORMANCE

In the previous chapters, the basic principles and practices were discussed with respect to accomplishment of 100 percent amplitude modulation. Other aspects of the ideal modulating objective were linearity and the use of a sine wave to modulate the carrier. This constitutes the "classical" approach; it best serves the requirements of mathematical analysis and of academic standardization. Nonetheless, practical modulating techniques have evolved considerably around departures from such textbook design philosophy. The reasons for this are readily evidenced by the following example.

THE INHERENT INEFFICIENCY OF AMPLITUDE-MODULATION TRANSMITTERS

Assume that a radiotelephone transmitter is to have an unmodulated carrier output of 100 watts. The modulator must have capability to completely modulate the carrier with a sine wave. A single-ended class-A modulator using a triode tube is selected. It plate modulates a single-ended class-C amplifier having a plate efficiency of 75 percent. The efficiency of the modulator is 33.3 percent. These facts dictate a need for 66.7 watts of modulating output power to affect 100 percent modulation of the 133.3 watts of d-c input power to the class-C amplifier. Under these conditions, the d-c input power which must be constantly supplied to the modulator is 200 watts.

The total d-c power required by the class-C amplifier and the modulator is 333.3 watts. Considering the needs of the remainder of the transmitter comprising oscillator, buffer amplifiers, speech amplifiers, filament heater power, and auxiliary circuitry, one could reasonably postulate a total operating power requirement of 400 watts. Allowing for an overall conversion efficiency of 70 percent in the power supply system, we find that 571 watts must be consumed from the a-c line in order to operate such a transmitter. Now, let us see what return is received for such an investment.

With 100 percent sine-wave modulation, the carrier output power becomes 150 watts. The additional 50 watts in the modulated carrier is equally distributed between the two sidebands. One sideband is redundant with respect to the need to convey modulating intelligence. This leaves us with 25 watts of information-bearing power. Now, in actual use, the transmitter will handle speech, not sine-wave modulation. Speech waves are known to have about one-half as much average power as equal-peak-amplitude sine waves. Recall that peak amplitude of the modulating signal establishes the operating limits for 100 percent modulation. It can be thereby appreciated that the power added to the sidebands with speech modulation will be half that pertaining to sine-wave modulation. Thus, we reduce the power invested in our single information-bearing sideband to 12½ watts. Inasmuch as most speakers do not talk without restive pauses, we may take this into account by reducing the average power in this sideband to, say, ten watts. Nor are we yet finished in our obvious task of belittling the performance of this transmitter. Unless special techniques are employed, it falls short of reality to suppose that a speaker can continuously 100 percent modulate the carrier with speech. The transient nature of speech waves precludes this, as also does the inordinate skill required to maintain optimum speaking volume and distance from the microphone. Let it be estimated that the transmitter will, on the average, be 40 percent modulated. The ten watts of information-bearing power must now be reduced by the factor 0.4^2, or 0.16. We finally find that, for the 571 watts of power drawn from the a-c mains, we produce 1.6 watts of basic "talking power." Summarizing further, we note that the 100-watt carrier conveys no modulating information. Moreover, 133.3 watts are constantly used to heat the plate of the modulating tubes whether or not the microphone is actuated. Also, 33.3 watts are constantly dissipated in the plate of the modulated class-C amplifier. From an overall functional viewpoint, it appears that we have a fairly good room-heater which produces a high-frequency carrier as a major by-product and an information-bearing component as an incidental by-product.

Nor would the picture be necessarily more encouraging with low-level modulation. What we would eliminate in modulator dissipation, we would approximately gain in dissipation of the efficiency-modulated class-C amplifier. The practical difficulties in achieving 100 percent linear modulation invariably are reflected as an increase in overall power input. Generally, more additional power is required for swamping techniques in both r-f and audio circuits and for well-regulated bias supplies than in high-level modulation. In low-level modulation, it is often necessary to employ an additional buffer stage in the r-f section in order to maintain good isolation from the oscillator. Otherwise, much the same analysis applies, and both modulating systems must be described as very inefficient converters of a-c power to "talking power."

Our brief appraisal of the operating conditions of a "classically" designed radiotelephone transmitter enables us to suggest improvements. The following is a compilation of modifications intended to increase the effectiveness of amplitude modulation:

1. Increase the efficiency of the modulated amplifier.
2. Increase the efficiency of the modulator.
3. Increase the efficiency of the power supply.
4. Disconnect modulator input power when there is no modulation.
5. Automatically maintain modulation factor near 100 percent.
6. Transmit carrier and one sideband only.
7. Transmit both sidebands, but suppress carrier.
8. Transmit one sideband only.
9. Modulate only with those frequency components of speech which make the greatest contribution to intelligibility.
10. Control carrier power in accordance with strength of modulating signal.

In the following discussions, various techniques will be discussed to bring about such improvements as listed above. No particular sequence will be adhered to, but each improvement technique is intended to be an application independent of all others. In many transmitter situations, it will obviously be possible to incorporate more than one improvement, thereby achieving even greater advantage over the unmodified "classical" transmitter.

DISADVANTAGES OF THE SINGLE-ENDED CLASS-A MODULATOR

Actually, the 100-watt single-ended modulator postulated for the "classically" designed transmitter has been considered unrealistic since the early days of broadcasting. At the present time, single-ended class-A power stages have been retained for the output of radio receivers and for modulation of low-power transmitters such as those employed on the citizens band. Even for these applications, the principal motivating factor is initial economy of components. The single-ended class-A amplifier inherently suffers from the following shortcomings:

1. Low efficiency. Maximum theoretical efficiency is 50 percent. Because of high distortion from the lower portion of the tube transfer characteristic, the dynamic range (plate current swing) must be restricted. In practice, the efficiency is generally from 30 to 35 percent. It should be mentioned, however, that the transistor class-A power amplifier can readily develop efficiencies exceeding 46 percent.

2. Conflict between low-frequency response and output transformer size. This conflict exists with any amplifier, but it is considerably agitated by the single-ended class-A amplifier. This is due to the fact that the d-c plate current tends to saturate the core. Low frequencies suffer power attenuation first when the transformer inductance decreases from the effects of saturation. Thus, two reasons compel the need for a large transformer, these being the reduction of magnetic saturation effects and the requirements of low-frequency response.

3. Early power limit due to excessive distortion. Both the curvature in the low-current range of the transfer characteristic and the saturation of the transformer core produce unacceptable amounts of second and higher even-order harmonics when an attempt is made to increase output and efficiency.

4. Dependency on power supply for completion of signal-frequency circuits. The fact that signal-frequency currents through the power supply to the single-ended class-A amplifier places the supply in the roll of common impedance to all amplifier stages which it energizes. This leads to difficult oscillatory situations which must be remedied by decoupling networks and, in aggravated cases, by separate d-c supplies. Even after interstage coupling has been reduced below the possibility of oscillation, the frequency response of the single-ended power amplifier depends on power supply impedance. Also, there is considerable susceptibility to hum superimposed on the d-c supply current.

BASIC OPERATING FEATURES OF PUSH-PULL AMPLIFICATION

Push-pull amplifiers are characterized by the following features:

1. Two amplifying elements are utilized.
2. The grids, or input electrodes, of the two amplifying ele-

ments are excited with equal voltages 180 degrees out of phase with one another.

3. The two elements alternate conduction roles throughout the signal cycle. While one element is consuming increasing current, the other element is decreasing its current consumption. At half-cycle intervals, the conduction states are interchanged.

4. The current outputs from the two amplifying elements are combined in an output transformer. The combining process is such that, even though the *individual* waveforms from the amplifying elements deviate from the input signal waveshape, a waveshape replica of the original signal is available from the secondary winding of the output transformer.

5. Output-transformer core magnetization is cancelled by opposing fields developed in the two halves of the primary. This implies a physically smaller transformer and better low-frequency response.

6. Circuit arrangement tends to cancel even-order harmonics. This implies extended plate current swing, even encompassing very nonlinear portions of the transfer characteristics. Therefore, the push-pull power amplifier *more than doubles* the power obtainable from a single amplifying element for the same percentage of distortion.

7. The push-pull circuit does not require bypassing of bias sources. There are no signal-frequency currents through the d-c power supply. Thus, the power supply does not behave as a common impedance with respect to earlier amplifier stages. This greatly discourages the tendency toward motorboating and interstage oscillation. No decoupling networks are required in ordinary applications.

8. With the push-pull arrangement, hum superimposed on the d-c power supply is largely cancelled out.

Class-AB and Class-B Push-Pull Modulators

It has been mentioned that the push-pull circuit inherently restores the original waveshape even though the waveshape of the individual amplifying elements deviate from the original. This feature may be exploited all the way to the condition where each amplifying element responds to only one half-cycle of the original waveform. Despite such rectifierlike action, the output transformer will combine the two half-cycles so that a full-cycle replica of the original wave is available from the transformer secondary. This extreme case corresponds to class-B operation. The elements are biased so that they draw no current when there is no signal input. This, in itself, is a tremendous advantage. It will be recalled that the class-A amplifier produces constant plate (or collector) dissipation with or without signal input. Not only is the plate current of the class-B amplifier made to swing with the input signal, but the grids are driven into their positive region. Thus, a class-B amplifier consumes power from its driver stage. This technique squeezes the optimum amount of power from the stage. A push-pull class-B modulator so operated has a maximum attainable efficiency of 78 percent when excited to full output. The beauty of the class-B modulator is that its power output and efficiency go up together; when no

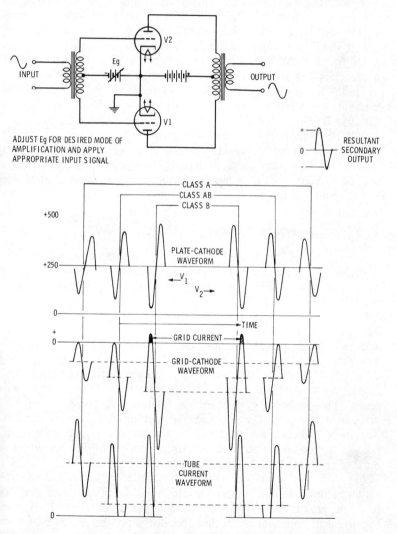

Fig. 4-1. Generalized push-pull modulator.

speech is being handled, the tubes idle at zero output and virtually zero input.

In order to avoid certain difficulties inherent in driving class-B amplifiers, and to reduce crossover distortion (commutating transients accompanying switching from one tube to the other), tubes are often operated in compromise modes; that is, somewhere *between* class A and class B. Considerable improvement in operating efficiency is obtained from class-AB operation in that plate current does not occur in each tube during the entire input cycle, but no grid current is allowed either. Fig. 4-1 shows waveshapes in class-A, AB, and B operation. The overall efficiency of such a modulator system should also take into account the lack of driving power required for class-AB operation. The d-c plate input power and current to the class-AB modulator is not zero with no input signal, but is profitably lower than with class-A operation. Fig. 4-2 shows the generalized operating mode for push-pull modulators in class-A, AB, and B.

With transistor modulators, it is generally expedient to exploit the full possibilities of class-B operation, or very nearly so. This is because the transistor demands input signal power whether it operates class-A or class-B. Class-B operation is, of course, ideal for battery conservation in portable equipment.

POLARIZATION OF SPEECH WAVES

Speech waves tend to be somewhat unsymmetrical near the zero axis. This implies that, depending on how such polarization is used, an excess of either outward or inward envelope modulation is possible. The choice of such matters is readily made by phasing either primary or secondary leads of any transformer in the modulation system one way or the other. Excessive inward (negative) modulation is to be avoided because the outward (positive) modulation will then be limited to something less than 100 percent. On the other hand, if the polarization is such that excessive outward modulation of the envelope occurs, much greater "talking power" will result. This is because outward modulation will then exceed 100 percent when inward modulation is just limited to 100 percent. The basic principle involved here is that distortion and splatter do not occur from outward modulations greater than 100 percent, but only when inward modulation exceeds 100 percent.

Fig. 4-3 shows an unsymmetrical modulating wave and the resultant amplitude-modulation pattern when polarization is such as to allow greater than 100 percent outward modulation. It is very important to understand that this does not imply the presence of nonlinearity such as described by carrier-level shift. If a modulation

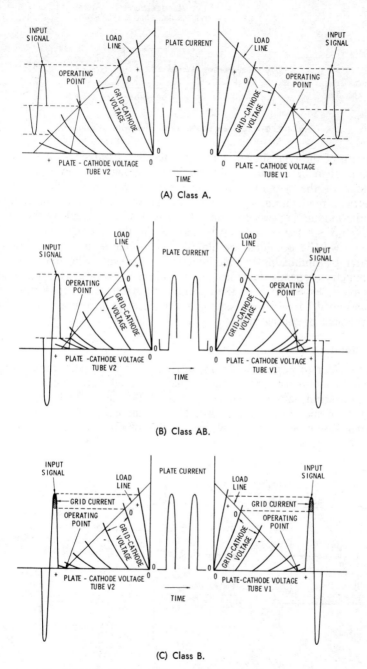

(A) Class A.

(B) Class AB.

(C) Class B.

Fig. 4-2. Generalized operational mode for push-pull amplifiers.

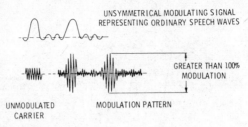

UNSYMMETRICAL MODULATING SIGNAL
REPRESENTING ORDINARY SPEECH WAVES

GREATER THAN 100%
MODULATION

UNMODULATED
CARRIER

MODULATION PATTERN

Fig. 4-3. Greater than 100% modulation without splatter.

pattern of the type shown in Fig. 4-3 resulted from sine-wave modulation, then carrier-level shift would be present. However, the envelope of the pattern shown here exactly reproduces the unsymmetrical modulating signal. For this reason, no distortion occurs in the modulating process. Since the envelope is not cut by the zero axis, no splatter occurs. An increase in the average modulating factor will be obtained for almost any amplitude-modulated transmitter by optimizing the modulation in this way. The deviation in symmetry depends on the microphone and varies with different speakers. However, once the optimum polarization is experimentally determined for a given system, it can then be incorporated as the permanent operating mode.

Modulation Monitor

In order to achieve optimum talking power, the peak modulating factor should just approach, but never exceed 100 percent in the inward (or negative) modulating interval. Due to the highly transient nature of speech waveforms, it is almost mandatory that some visual means be employed to enable monitoring of this condition. Fig. 4-4 shows a simple modulation monitor. When negative modulation peaks

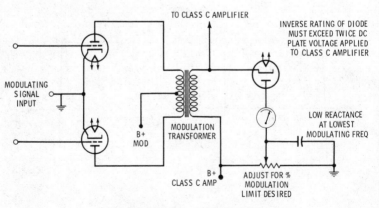

Fig. 4-4. Negative-modulation monitor.

exceed 100 percent or preferably a somewhat lower limit, the diode will be provided with forward conduction bias and the meter will deflect. The potentiometer enables selection of the modulating factor at which meter deflection will occur. If the slider is all the way to the right, the meter will not deflect until inward modulation just exceeds 100 percent. If the slider is moved to the left, the plate of the diode is more readily made positive with respect to its cathode. Under such a condition, the meter can be adjusted to provide a warning deflection at modulation factors of 90 percent or 95 percent.

When this monitor is used, the gain control of the speech amplifier is advanced during normal speech until occasional meter deflections are observed. It is important to spend some time with familiarization and calibration of the monitor. Calibration can be accomplished with sine-wave modulation by comparing results of potentiometer adjustments with the information presented by either the trapezoid or amplitude-modulation pattern on the oscilloscope. This monitor does not indicate modulation limits for outward (or positive) modulation. Inasmuch as outward modulation in excess of 100 percent causes neither splatter nor distortion if modulation is otherwise linear, this is generally not a matter of concern. Indeed, as explained in the discussion on speech polarization, a worthwhile increase in talking power can be brought about with greater than 100 percent outward modulation. For any given system, the use of a modulation monitor in conjunction with determination of optimum speech polarity can provide considerably improved performance without actual design changes.

CONTROLLED CARRIER SYSTEM

The carrier component of an amplitude-modulated wave conveys no modulating information. At 100 percent modulation, the carrier is invested with two-thirds of the total power in the modulated wave. At lower modulating factors, the preponderance of power in the carrier component is very much greater. If the carrier power could be reduced during shallow modulation intervals, two worthwhile things would be accomplished. First, the average plate dissipation of the modulated class-C amplifier would be considerably reduced. The tube would then be called on to produce carrier power only as needed. Secondly, the average modulating factor would be increased. This can result in enhanced detection efficiency at the receiver. Such modulated amplifier operation is produced by controlled carrier techniques. In controlled carrier modulation, the modulating factor is maintained at a near-constant and relatively high value. Low-level speech is accompanied by low-level carrier output. High-level speech produces an appropriately stronger carrier.

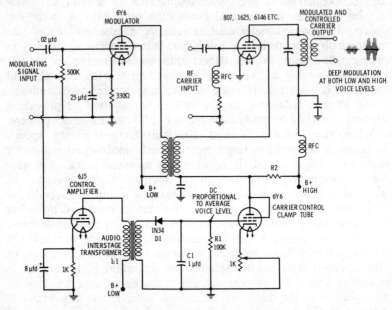

Fig. 4-5. Circuit for obtaining controlled carrier.

Fig. 4-5 shows a circuit for achieving controlled carrier operation. This circuit does not represent the simplest approach, but is a systematic and readily adjusted method. Each function is independently provided by a circuit section. This is superior to apparently simpler approaches, one of which combines all functions in a single modulator tube. In Fig. 4-5 it is shown that actual speech modulation is provided by transformer-coupled screen-grid modulation. The other tubes and associated circuitry are concerned with the control of d-c screen-grid voltage to the modulated class-C amplifier. This control, in turn, governs carrier output power. Such control is inflected in terms of the *average* amplitude of the modulating signal. This is in contradiction to the screen-grid modulating voltage derived from the modulation transformer where control (i.e., modulation) follows the *instantaneous* amplitude of the modulating signal.

Note that a portion of the modulating signal from microphone or speech amplifier is separately amplified in the control amplifier. Rectifier D1 then converts the amplified speech signal to negative grid bias for the clamp tube. This d-c grid bias cannot follow the instantaneous fluctuations of the speech signal due to the time constant imposed by resistance-capacitance network, R1-C1. The relatively slow control exerted over the clamp-tube shunt controls the d-c voltage applied to the screen grid of the modulated class-C amplifier. When the speech amplitude is sustained at a high level over a number of syllables, the clamp tube receives increased negative grid bias. This relaxes its shunting action in the screen-grid circuit of the modulated amplifier. The increased d-c screen-grid voltage thereby enables generation of higher carrier output power. It is shown that the clamp tube forms the variable arm of a potentiometer with respect to resistance R2. When speech amplitude has been at low level for sufficient time, the clamp tube receives lower negative grid bias. The clamp tube then has a lowered plate-cathode resistance and exerts increased shunting action. The d-c screen-grid voltage to the modulated amplifier is thereby lowered, as is the carrier output power generated by it.

Reception of controlled carrier signals plays havoc with the automatic volume control system of some receivers. If the time constant of the feedback path in the automatic control circuit is too short, severe distortion will result. The time constant must be sufficiently long to minimize the tendency of the receiver gain to follow variations in level of the controlled carrier signal.

SPEECH CLIPPING

With 100 percent sine-wave modulation, two-thirds of the power resides in the carrier component and the remaining third is shared by the two sidebands. With 100 percent *speech* modulation an even more unfavorable distribution of power exists. It is then found that the sidebands share only about one-fifth of the total power. This is because speech waves have a higher ratio of peak to average power than do sine waves. Peak power values establish the 100 percent modulating factor, but *average* power determines the relative effectiveness in conveying modulating information. This being the case, it would be profitable to modify speech waveshapes in the direction of greater average-to-peak power ratios. This is readily brought about by clipping the narrow spike characteristic of speech waves, thereby producing a wave train comprised of relatively wide rectangular pulses. Such a technique of course is directly contradictory to the pains taken to preserve all features of waves in most sound equipment. Although clipping does indeed alter the characteristics of speech, actual intelligibility is not significantly degraded with surprisingly severe alteration of the original speech waves. Clipped speech affords another advantage due to the more nearly constant peak amplitude of such wave compared with the wide range of peak amplitudes residing in natural speech waves. This means that the 100 percent modulation adjustment of the modulated amplifier can be made in terms of a frequently occuring modulating signal level rather than an occasionally occuring one. This situation, too, increases the average power in the sidebands. Once a transmitter incorporating speech clipping is properly adjusted, overmodulation cannot occur. This, itself, often justifies its use.

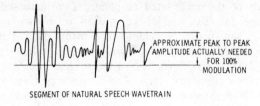

SEGMENT OF NATURAL SPEECH WAVETRAIN

RESULT OF CLIPPING

MODULATION SPLATTER
COULD BE CAUSED
AT ANY PART OF THE WAVEFORM
THAT IS CLIPPED

WAVEFORM RESULTING FROM PASSAGE THROUGH LOW PASS FILTER

Fig. 4-6. Waveforms involved in speech clipping and filtering.

It would not be permissible to simply insert a speech-clipping stage in the speech amplifier. The process of clipping is accompanied by wide-band harmonic generation. Thus, the clipper tends to produce modulation splatter in a manner which for practical effects is quite similar to that ordinarily attributed to overmodulation. Fortunately, these harmonics can be prevented from reaching the modulator. This is accomplished by following the speech clipper with a low-pass filter. The low-pass filter is designed to pass speech-frequency components, say to 3500 cps, but to reject the higher, splatter-producing frequencies. Wave forms involved in speech clipping are shown in Fig. 4-6. A representative circuit is shown in Fig. 4-7. In this circuit the diode section concerned with the clipping of the positive-going speech waveform is biased to cause less severe clipping than is accorded the negative-going portions.

A practical difficulty often encountered with speech clipping is due to inadequate low-frequency response of the modulation transformer. When the quasi-rectangular pulse of the clipped speech waves pass through such a transformer, they become peaked again. This, of course, tends to defeat the sought objectives. A remedial technique for such a situation, if not too severe, is to apply a modu-

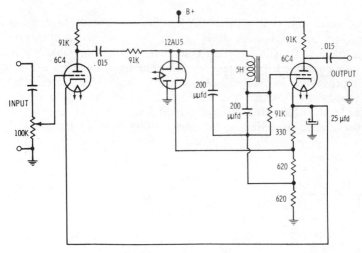

Fig. 4-7. Speech clipper and filter circuit.

lation-envelope feedback loop between the transmitter output and an early speech amplifier stage. Such a feedback loop must contain a linear detector and must be phased for negative feedback. This technique is shown in Fig. 4-10 and is described in the accompanying discussion. When such a feedback loop is used, even greater emphasis is placed on the low-pass filter to attenuate splatter producing harmonics generated by the clipping process. This is because one of the features of negative feedback is that the response characteristics of frequency-selective circuits tends to be smoothed out. Another remedy is the attenuation of speech frequencies lower than 500 cps *prior* to clipping.

Another way to accomplish speech clipping is to cause the class-B modulator tubes to saturate at a power level corresponding to nearly 100 percent modulation. This can be brought about by adjustment of the plate to plate load impedance. Generally, this involves a hand-wound transformer with a number of taps. Also, some control over the saturation point is afforded by adjustment of the plate voltage to plate current ratio of the modulated amplifier. The determination may be tedious and time consuming, but, once attained, it should prove very worthwhile. A low-pass filter must be inserted between the secondary of the modulation transformer and the modulated amplifier. Such high-level clipping can yield very effective performance.

SPEECH COMPRESSION

After a simple radiotelephone transmitter is adjusted for proper operation, the maintenance of high "talking power" is considerably a function of the skill of the speaker. It is not easy to constantly speak at optimum voice level, or at the best distance from the microphone. To alleviate this condition, the speech amplifier may be gain-controlled by average speech amplitude. Such an automatic gain provision delivers substantially the same signal amplitude to the modulator whether the microphone picks up strong or weak voice levels. Many circuits have been devised for accomplishing such control. Most are based on the concept illustrated by the block dia-

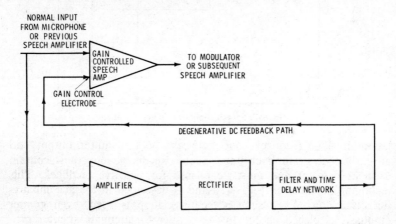

Fig. 4-8. Basic speech-compression system.

gram of Fig. 4-8. Speech frequencies are amplified, then rectified, and applied to an RC filter. The d-c voltage developed across the filter output follows the *average* amplitude of the speech waveform. The d-c voltage is so polarized that a negative-feedback loop results when it is applied to an appropriate control electrode of a speech amplifier stage. Thus, *high*-level speech *reduces* the gain of the controlled speech amplifier.

The operating characteristics of such speech compressors are somewhat an admixture of art and science. Obviously, the gain should not fluctuate with the syllabic rate of speech. Within this limit, it is desirable that response to changed average level be fairly rapid. Somewhat in conflict is the desirability of a "memory" so that a gain change is preserved beyond the stimulus producing it. This prevents a disagreeable rise in background noise between words.

Fig. 4-9 is a representative circuit for accomplishing the functions depicted in the block diagram of Fig. 4-8. Additionally, a threshold control is provided to inhibit speech compression below a certain speech amplitude. This is done by back-biasing the diodes.

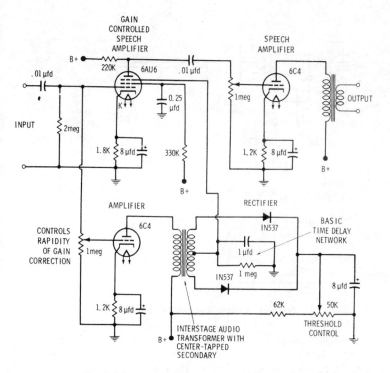

Fig. 4-9. Representative speech-compression circuit.

MODULATION-ENVELOPE FEEDBACK

The modulating linearity of transmitters, particularly those employing low-level modulation, can be considerably improved by means of a degenerative feedback loop providing a path from the output of the transmitter to the first, or to an early, speech amplifier stage. A linear detector is interposed within this feedback loop so that the fed-back signal is at the modulation frequency. A first requisite of such a degenerative feedback technique is that of phasing. The proper phasing polarity for negative feedback will depend on the total number of amplifier stages (and type of interstage coupling) enclosed by the loop. In order to make an envelope feedback circuit universally applicable, a phase-selecting switch is incorporated. This is shown in the modulation-envelope feedback circuit of Fig. 4-10. Even when proper phasing for negative feedback is determined for the particular equipment, there will be a limited amount of such feedback which can be utilized. Potentiometer R1 enables adjustment of the amount of negative feedback. A trape-

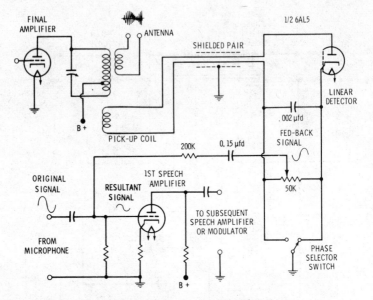

Fig. 4-10. Modulation-envelope feedback circuit.

zoidal pattern should be monitored on an oscilloscope for such adjustment. It should be possible to change any curvatures in the trapezoid to straight-sided slopes. Such a change indicates linearization of the modulating process. If such improvement is not forthcoming, it is suggestive of serious malperformance in the modulator or speech amplifiers.

This technique readily benefits grid-bias, screen-grid, and suppressor-grid modulated transmitters. On the other hand, some difficulty can be anticipated with plate modulated transmitters employing class-B modulators. The leakage reactance of the class-B modulation transformer often imposes an early limit to the amount of remedial negative feedback which can be accommodated.

HIGH-LEVEL SPLATTER SUPPRESSOR

A plate modulated class-C amplifier often has extended modulating capability in the outward, or positive, direction. Even when linearity suffers, good communications intelligibility prevails long after the loss of "hi-fi" reproduction of the modulating signal. There are generally three limiting factors to such extended modulation. First, it is not permissible to exceed 100 percent modulation in the inward, or negative, direction. Such operation is prohibitive because numerous spurious sidebands are generated. These sidebands cover considerably more spectrum space than do the side-

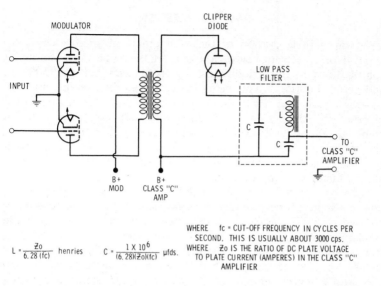

$$L = \frac{Zo}{6.28\,(fc)} \text{ henries} \qquad C = \frac{1 \times 10^{6}}{(6.28)(Zo)(fc)} \text{ } \mu fds.$$

WHERE   fc = CUT-OFF FREQUENCY IN CYCLES PER SECOND. THIS IS USUALLY ABOUT 3000 cps.
WHERE   Zo IS THE RATIO OF DC PLATE VOLTAGE TO PLATE CURRENT (AMPERES) IN THE CLASS "C" AMPLIFIER

Fig. 4-11. High-level splatter-suppressor circuit.

bands of proper speech modulation. As a consequence, severe interference with the operation of other stations is produced. Secondly, extended outward, or positive, modulation can exceed the peak plate voltage the modulated tube is capable of safely withstanding. Finally, some tubes may have their average power rating stressed by such modulation. A technique will be described which effectively removes the first limiting factor. Whether the second or third limitations exist will have to be determined by the tubes and operating voltages employed in individual systems. It is an open secret that considerable overloading is often the case with amateur transmitters. This may not be too objectionable if the resultant trade-off for reduced tube longevity is willingly accepted. However, pains should be taken to ensure against catastrophic arcovers or breakdowns.

The circuit of Fig. 4-11 permits any degree of modulation in the outward, or positive, direction. The diode limits modulation in the inward, or negative, direction to approximately 100 percent, however. Even so, the abrupt interruption of a high-amplitude, negative, modulating wave would produce wideband harmonics in the spectrum of the modulated carrier. Therefore, a low-pass filter is interposed between the diode and the plate supply lead to the modulated amplifier. The filter passes speech frequencies up to about 3500 cps, but rejects all higher frequencies.

BASS SUPPRESSION

A considerable portion of the total power of speech waves resides in the spectrum below 500 cps. At the same time, the major contributions to intelligibility are by frequencies between 500 cps and about 3,000 cps. This being the case, less than optimum "talk" power" is achieved if the frequencies below 500 cps are permitted to establish 100 percent modulating limits. It would be better to eliminate, or at least attenuate, the speech frequencies below 500 cps. Then, the more effective frequencies in the 500-cps to 3000-cps range could be increased in amplitude until the 100 percent modulating factor was approached.

Such operation is readily brought about simply by reducing the time constant of the coupling capacitor and grid leak in resistance-coupled speech amplifiers. When two such cascaded stages are "undercoupled" in this manner for low-speech frequencies, the effect is quite pronounced. Degradation of low-frequency audio response can also be accomplished by adding an audio choke in parallel with a speech amplifier grid leak, or by the use of skimpy bypass capacitors across cathode resistors. In any event, it is generally undesirable to employ negative feedback around speech amplifier stages intended to provide bass suppression. Such feedback would tend to flatten out the frequency response of the overall speech amplifier system.

Another dividend conferred by bass suppression is the possible use of smaller and lighter iron core components in the speech amplifier and modulator circuits. For a given power-handling capacity, transformers must be larger for lower frequencies. The converse of this situation is that bass suppression could be initially achieved by deliberately selecting transformers with drooping low-frequency response. Bass suppression is particularly profitable when employed prior to speech clipping.

Sometimes it also is beneficial to provide attenuation for audio frequencies beyond about 3000 cps. The advantage is not as great as for bass suppression, however. High-frequency attenuation is sometimes useful in reducing interfering noises which find their way into the modulating system through the power line or by other means. Also, the characteristic hiss from carbon-granule microphones can be discriminated against by limiting high-frequency response.

THE BIAS-SHIFT CLASS-A MODULATOR

In the conventional class-A audio amplifier or modulator, the plate dissipation is constant. Even when no speech is being amplified, the plate converts as much electrical energy into heat as when maximum power output is being developed. The irony of this situation is that the plate input power during amplification of low-intensity speech signals actually *need not* be as high as when the amplifier is driven to maximum output. Thus ordinary class-A operation is inherently wasteful under typical speech service. If, on the other hand, some means were incorporated to *automatically* change the operating point according to the plate current swing actually required, class-A operation would be retained but with greatly increased overall efficiency.

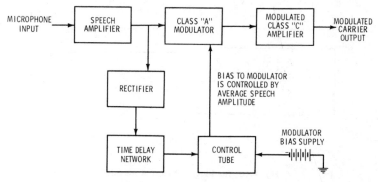

Fig. 4-12. Bias-shift system for increasing plate efficiency of a class-A modulator.

The bias-shift modulator does just this. The improvement in efficiency is so great that practical circuits take the form of revised Heising modulation schemes. Such a single-ended modulator dispenses with expensive modulation transformers and requires virtually no driving power. The block diagram underlying this concept is shown in Fig. 4-12. A representative schematic diagram is illustrated by Fig. 4-13. The basic function is provided by the bias-control tube. In response to the d-c level of rectified speech waves, this tube governs the amount of negative grid bias alloted to the bias-shift modulator. For *low-intensity speech,* the bias-control tube is relatively conductive with the result that a large portion of the negative voltage developed by the modulator bias supply is actually applied to the grid of the bias-shift modulator. Therefore, the modulator does not consume the high plate current that it would if its operating point were fixed by the requirements of maximum power capability. For *high-intensity speech,* the bias-control tube becomes *less* conductive by virtue of the larger negative bias applied to its grid from rectification of the speech signal. In turn, the grid of the bias-shift modulator becomes less negative. This allows increased plate current so that the modulator can develop the increased output demand. The control tube is a small receiving type even for large modulators.

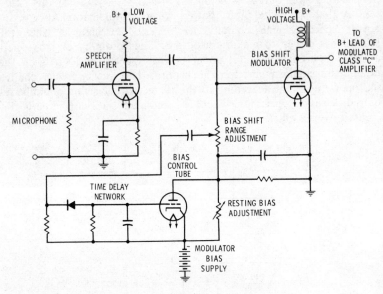

Fig. 4-13. The bias-shift class-A modulator.

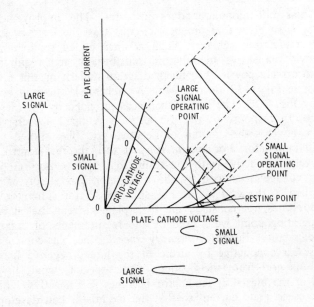

Fig. 4-14. Operation of bias-shift class-A modulator.

Such bias-shifting in terms of demand is shown in Fig. 4-14. Note that true class-A operation prevails for both the small signal and the large signal. Yet, the "steady" d-c plate current for the small signal is very much less than for the large signal.

It is important that the response to the sensing of the speech amplitude be delayed. Instantaneous response would produce severe distortion in the modulator and would defeat the basic objective of this arrangement. The operating point of the modulator should change in accordance with the average intensity of speech and no faster than the syllabic rate. Such delayed response is provided by the simple RC time-delay network shown in Fig. 4-13.

USE OF LINEAR AMPLIFIER TO INCREASE MODULATING FACTOR

A linear amplifier is truly linear when operated between class-B and class-A. Class-B operation yields the best plate efficiency. Class-AB$_1$ operation gives good plate efficiency and makes little demand on the driving stage. The descriptive term "linear" implies faithful reproduction of the modulation envelope. It is in this meaning that the class-C amplifier is unsatisfactory for boosting the power level of modulated waves. However, a unique advantage may be

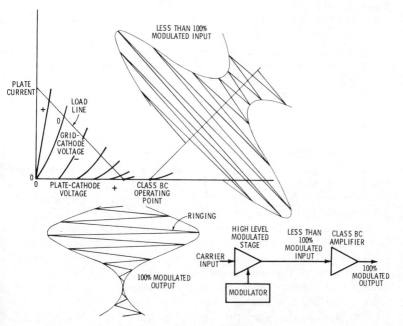

Fig. 4-15. Use of the class-BC amplifier to increase modulation factor.

had from the operation of an amplifier with slightly more negative bias then is required for class-B operation. Such a class-BC amplifier has the property of increasing the modulation factor of the applied modulated carrier. In so doing, it no longer operates strictly as a linear amplifier. However, the distortion imparted to the modulation envelope need not appreciably degrade the intelligiblity of speech if the stretching of modulation factor is not too drastic. An increase from 70 percent to the vicinity of 100 percent is practical for communications systems.

Fig. 4-15 shows the way in which the class-BC amplifier stretches the modulation factor. Such an amplifier requires tight control of all operating parameters. In the example shown, it can be seen that a slight increase in modulating factor in the input will produce output envelope distortion. Although such modulation stretching does not represent a commonplace design technique, this phenomenon often occurs inadvertently in practical linear amplifiers.

RCDS AMPLITUDE MODULATION

Commercial services, carrier-frequency telephony, amateur radio, and the citizens band all have had some involvement with a form of amplitude modulation known as *rcds*. This abbreviation stands for *reduced-carrier double-sideband* and is self-explanatory. It is quite obvious that double sideband *suppressed*-carrier operation, such as would be obtained with a balanced modulator output stage would offer the advantage that all of the generated output power would be invested in the information-bearing sidebands. This, indeed, constitutes a great gain in terms of transmitter power conversion efficiency. Unfortunately, however, such operation produces demodulation problems in the receiver. This is because the two sidebands alone do not combine to form an amplitude-modulation envelope. As a consequence, an artificial carrier must be inserted at the receiver. In actual practice this poses an inordinately critical tuning problem because both frequency and phase must simulate the carrier suppressed at the transmitter. Slight deviations from this result in relatively high distortion of the demodulated signal developed in the output circuit of the detectors.

This detection problem can be circumvented by transmitting a *reduced*-amplitude carrier. It is found that a usable amplitude-modulation pattern can be developed from a reduced carrier. This still vastly improves transmitter efficiency. The detector distortion is, under such circumstances, not detrimental to speech intelligence. What distortion is produced, can be considerably minimized by enhancing the carrier amplitude prior to detection. This is readily accomplished in modern receivers which provide panel controlled selectivities of the i-f passband. If the passband response is *narrower* than would ordinarily be employed to embrace the speech frequencies, more amplification can be imparted to the *carrier* than to the sideband. Then, when the received signal is finally presented to the second detector, the original amplitude relationship between carrier and sidebands will have been approximately restored to what it would have been had not the carrier been reduced in amplitude at the transmitter. The compensation cannot be exact, due to phase distortion produced by the narrow passband. However, the practical results for voice communications are exceedingly good.

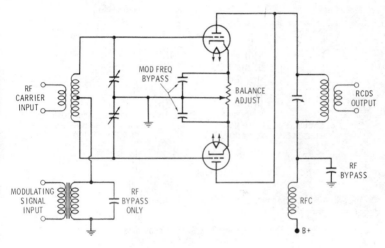

Fig. 4-16. Output stage for producing rcds amplitude modulation.

The rcds wave is generated by means of a balanced modulator configuration in which electrical imbalance is deliberately brought about. Fig. 4-16 gives an approach suitable for low-power transmitters. For higher-power service, good results are obtained from tetrodes in which the purposeful carrier "leak through" is produced by operating one screen grid at a higher voltage than the other. The modulation is then superimposed on the two screen grids. The rcds wave is developed across the resonant tank in the plate circuit. The circuit is essentially similar to the screen-grid balanced modulator shown in Chapter 3.

As a consequence of altering the "natural" relationship between carrier and sideband power in the a-m wave, the modulating factor of the rcds wave exceeds 100 percent. An equivalent modulating factor of about 400 percent has been used successfully. The reason this is possible without splatter generation may be inferred from Fig. 4-17. When the rcds wave envelope exceeds 100 percent modulation in the negative (inward) direction, a phase reversal occurs with *continuance* of the envelope in the opposite direction. Obviously, this does not constitute distortion of the modulating information. The significant point is that splatter is not generated as with the abrupt cessation of the envelope when the ordinary a-m wave exceeds 100 percent inward modulation. As mentioned previously, the distortion is not detrimental to intelligibility for equivalent modulating factor far exceeding 100 percent.

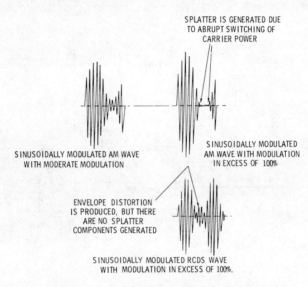

Fig. 4-17. Overmodulation in conventional and rcds amplitude modulation systems.

Rcds modulation can be amplified in linear amplifiers. It possesses the feature that little modulating power is required. In amateur radio, rcds. appears to have served the evolutionary purpose of serving as an intermediate step to single-sideband (SSB) transmission. At this writing, rcds transmission has appeared in some citizens band equipment as a means of making more effective use of the maximum legal power.

SINGLE SIDEBAND

A brief discussion of single-sideband modulation is the natural culmination of a treatise on amplitude modulation. The long, winding, and often digressing path of modulating techniques appears, in retrospect, to have had the main evolutionary goal of single-sideband modulation. Similarly, single-sideband modulation constitutes the logical end of this chapter. This is so because single-sideband modulation combines the greatest and most significant number of improvements over classical amplitude modulation.

In connection with several topics hitherto discussed, it has been pointed out that the conventional amplitude-modulated wave represents a wasteful modulating process. From the standpoint of transmission, it is necessary to invest two-thirds of generated power in the carrier, which conveys no modulating information. In actual practice, where speech rather than sine-wave modulation is used, and where the average modulating factor falls considerably short of 100 percent, it would be more accurate to say that the *preponderance* of power sent into the transmitting antenna goes into the carrier component. The relatively little "talk power" produced is redundantly divided between the two sidebands. From the standpoint of the receiver, somewhat more than twice the bandwidth is required to accommodate such a wave than would be needed to accept the spectrum inhabited by either the upper or lower sideband alone.

These considerations lead directly to thoughts of transmitting only a single sideband. Although it is known that either of the two "natural" sidebands of the amplitude-modulated wave suffice for transmission of the modulating information, it is also evident that deletion of the carrier and the alternative sideband would not leave us with a modulation envelope as feature of the transmitted wave. This most certainly must be anticipated as unpalatable "food" for the conventional a-m detector. However, let us first direct our attention to the production of single-sideband modulation at the transmitting end of the communications system. This will lead us to the requisite demodulating technique at the receiving station.

Methods of Generating Single-Sideband Signals

Two techniques are employed in the generation of the single-sideband signal. One is known as the *filter method,* the other as the *phasing method.* In the filter method, the carrier is first removed by a balanced modulator. Then one sideband is removed and the other passed by means of an appropriate bandpass filter. This suffices to produce the requisite single-sideband frequency spectrum in carrier telephone systems. In radiotelephony, this sequence of events is also used, but one or more frequency conversions must generally be effected in order to achieve the desired spectrum position. This is because the best filter performance is obtainable at low and moderate frequencies. Fig. 4-18 shows a filter method in conjunction with one frequency conversion. It should be realized that the filter method, as well as the phasing method to be described,

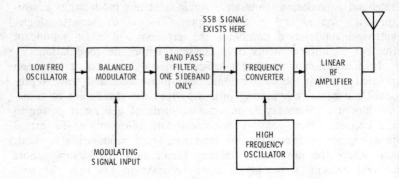

Fig. 4-18. Filter method of generating single sideband.

provide the function of frequency translation to the modulating signal. Thus, one might say that voice frequencies of 100 cps to 3,000 cps are translated to a frequency range of 1,000,100 cps to 1,003,000 cps.

The phasing method is illustrated by the block diagram of Fig. 4-19. The basic concept involved here is the generation of two double-sideband suppressed-carrier signals with such phase relations that the combining of these signals results in reinforcement of one sideband but cancellation of the other. In order to cause the balanced modulators to produce such signals, both the modulating frequencies and the carrier frequency applied to one balanced modulator must differ in phase by 90 degrees from the corresponding

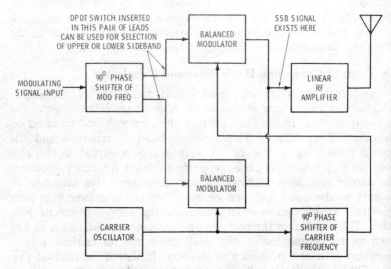

Fig. 4-19. Phasing method of generating single sideband.

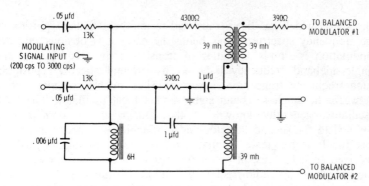

Fig. 4-20. 90° phase-shift network for speech-modulating frequencies.

frequencies applied to the other. Although a linear output amplifier is shown in Fig. 4-19, the phasing process can be accomplished at the level of the desired power output.

It should be appreciated that the 90-degree phase shift imparted to the input modulating signal applies to *all* of the voice frequencies involved. A special phase-shifting network is required to accomplish this. A unique feature of the phasing method is that a double-pole double-throw switch inserted in either pair of modulating signal leads to the balanced modulators enables selection of either the upper or the lower sideband. A representative network for achieving a 90-degree phase displacement throughout the main portion of the speech band is shown in Fig. 4-20. The requisite 90-degree phase displacement at the carrier frequency can be obtained from a much simpler network, such as is shown in Fig. 4-21.

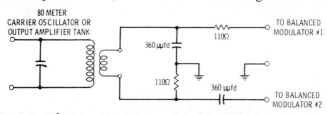

Fig. 4-21. 90° carrier phase-shift network for 80-meter amateur phone band.

Demodulation of Single-Sideband Signals

Demodulation of conventional amplitude-modulation signals is based on the detector's response to the modulation envelope. The modulation envelope is a composite wave made up of the vector addition of the carrier and the two sidebands. Inasmuch as the single-sideband signal comprises only one of these three components, there is no equivalent of the a-m envelope. The salient feature of the single-sideband signal is that it is a replica of the original modula-

157

ting signal which has been translated to another (higher) portion of the frequency spectrum. This being the case, it is obvious that demodulation is simply a matter of translating the frequency of the single-sideband frequency back to its original spectrum position. Such frequency translation is accomplished by heterodyning action between the single-sideband signal and a local oscillator. The local oscillator, generally known as the *beat-frequency oscillator,* is coupled to the second detector and is tunable. It is necessary to adjust the beat frequency oscillator for optimum intelligibility of the received speech. This, of course, corresponds to exact reinsertion of the speech in its audio-frequency domain. Fortunately, such carrier reinsertion makes no demand on phase. However, in certain commercial practices, it is not desirable to have to make and maintain such an adjustment. The need to manually adjust is then circumvented by transmitting a weak "pilot" carrier. At the receiving terminal, the pilot is separately amplified and then utilized to provide precise heterodyning for the demodulating process.

INDEX

2J3910